MULTICULTURAL EDUCATION RESOURCE GUIDE

by Cheryl Gorder

MULTICULTURAL EDUCATION RESOURCE GUIDE

by Cheryl Gorder

Published by:

BLUE BIRD PUBLISHING
1739 East Broadway #306
Tempe AZ 85202
(602) 831-6063

ISBN 0-933025-37-8 $12.95

Cover Art by Rob D. Wipprecht, Robin Graphic Designs

Library of Congress Cataloging-in-Publication Data

Gorder, Cheryl, 1952-
Multicultural education resource guide / by Cheryl Gorder .
p. cm.
Includes index.
ISBN 0-933025-37-8 (paper)
1. Multicultural education--United States--Directories.
2. Publishers and publishing--United States--Directories.
3. Associations, institutions, etc.--United States--Directories.
4. Corporations--United States--Directories. I. Title.
LC1099.3.G67 1995
370.19'6--dc20 95-37422
CIP

ABOUT THE AUTHOR

Cheryl Gorder is the author of several titles: *Home Schools: An Alternative*, a best-selling title on home education; *Homeless: Without Addresses in America,* which won a Benjamin Franklin award; *Green Earth Resource Guide*; and many more. She has been called upon by numerous radio and television stations to talk about home education, a specialty of hers.

She is the owner of Blue Bird Publishing, a company with titles emphasizing the family, education, and relationships. She also helps authors become self-publishers.

Cheryl and her daughter, Sarah, reside in Mesa, Arizona. Her boyfriend, Rob Wipprecht, has a cover design studio, and designed the cover on this book.

Contents

Learning About Diversity: What Parents and Teachers Can Do

by Dr. Francis Roberts

This article is reprinted from *Parents' Magazine*, May, 1992. Reprinted with permission from the author.

Recently I visited a first-grade classroom where there were a number of children whose first language was Spanish. Often such children do not feel like part of the mainstream until their English improves. But the teacher in this classroom had the sensitivity to reverse the situation. She was teaching the entire class some simple Spanish vocabulary. In the process, she was enlisting the aid of the newcomers, thus making them important resources in helping their classmates with the words that all of them now shared. To me, this was a good example of how schools can respond positively to the increasing cultural diversity of our country.

According to the 1990 census, the ethnic, nonwhite population of this country grew at least 16 percent during the 1980's. It is estimated that by the year 2000, 33 percent of the U.S. student population will be from so-called minority groups. The term "minority" is actually a misnomer, since in global terms, nonwhite peoples are in the majority; and this is also true of children in the public schools of many large cities, such as Los Angeles and Miami. Schools are challenged by the need to increase multicultural sensitivity and to reform their curricula to represent the ethnic diversity of their students.

Some academic and political leaders fear that America will split into a host of competing hostile groups based on racial or ethnic identity.

The goal of multicultural education is to prevent such splintering by teaching children to value and appreciate the rich and varied cultures that make up our nation. As parents and teachers we are in an excellent position to increase mutual respect and sensitivity and to reduce racism and other prejudices especially if we start early.

What Parents Can Do

Here are some specific ways that parents—at home and within their school district—can encourage children's appreciation of other cultures.

✓ Become sensitive to the language you use. One- to eight-year-olds are in their most active language learning years. What they hear sticks with them, for better or worse.

✓ Help children grow up with a global perspective, an understanding that there are many different cultures. All of us share the planet earth. Try to get a good-size globe or a world map along with a picture of the earth taken from space. When your child shows interest in an event or a person from another country, locate the place on the globe. If, for instance, your child has a new classmate from another part of the world, write the new child's name on a sticker and put it on the map or globe.

✓ Introduce your child to foods from different American cultures and traditions and explain why these foods are served. (You may have to do a little research first.) One Connecticut mother who likes to cook Tex-Mex-style food explained to her children that people in hot climates eat spicy foods because it makes them sweat and feel cooler. Another mother who often uses a wok to prepare stir-fry for her family explained to them how this healthy style of cooking originated in China.

- ✓ Note when there are special cultural festivals or celebrations in your area, and take the kids.
- ✓ Analyze your own friendships and relationships. If you have friends from different cultural groups, are your children acquainted with them? Seeing that parents have diverse friends has a very powerful influence on children.
- ✓ If your community is largely homogeneous, seek out new social outlets for your child, such as a summer camp, where there is more diversity.
- ✓ Encourage your PTA to start an in-school program that would include exchanges—in which elementary school students from different areas visit each other's classrooms—and more informed and extensive study of others cultures in the curriculum.
- ✓ Help your school establish partnerships with other schools, both in the United States and worldwide. Remember penpals. Nowadays, children can also make contact with each other via video and audiotape. Schools in my district have exchanged letter and tapes with a school in Moscow and artwork with one in Japan.
- ✓ Be honest with your children about history. Liberty and justice have not always been for all, and still are not. Women were not guaranteed the constitutional right to vote until the adoption of the Nineteenth Amendment in 1920 and black Americans were denied the full rights of citizenship until the much more recent civil-rights laws. Unfortunately, many forms of discrimination remain commonplace today.

✓ If you or your spouse belongs to a minority group, which is true of almost 25 percent of the U.S. population, help your children explore their cultural heritage. Children's self-esteem is enhanced when they know and appreciate their roots.

✓ Check the resources at the public library, most of which now list multicultural books and videos that you can borrow. Reading stories together gives you and your children an opportunity to discuss how everyday life is portrayed in different cultural settings.

✓ Depending on your children's ages, allow them to watch controversial news on TV. For example, don't protect them from broadcasts of racial violence, but view the news together, talk with them afterward, and let them share their concerns.

✓ Examine your own feelings about race and ethnicity. Each of us is the product of our own culture and experiences. Rather than turn your back on change, use the opportunity of educating your children to increase your own understanding.

What Schools Can Do

Schools, of course, can play a big part in helping children become more sensitive to cultural differences. But sensitivity must start with teachers and other school personnel and they may need assistance. Some schools run staff workshops to build teachers' understanding and to teach cultural sensitivity skills that they can use in the classroom. [Editor's note: Sources for these types of training sessions are included in this book.] For example, parental attitudes toward such issues as school discipline and homework vary widely across cultures. Teachers need to be acquainted with how children from different cultures respond to various learning methods so that they can meet the needs of these students and communicate better with parents. In all planning for staff development, it is crucial to involve custodians, secretaries, and others on staff who are in regular contact with children.

In some schools that have a rapid influx of culturally diverse kids, intergroup tensions may increase. At such times, the leadership of the principal is crucial. He or she might form a human-relations committee—including parents, faculty and students—to promote understanding among different groups in the community. Such committees have successfully planned activities such as potluck dinners, faculty-to-family visits, and workshops for parents and staff.

Teaching Children to Respect Diversity

by Gwendolyn Calvert Baker

Children deserve the best we can give them. They deserve plenty of nourishing food, access to health care and a safe place to live. They deserve our protection from exploitation, war and other sources of physical and mental harm. They deserve to live in a world free of discrimination and to receive an education that will help them be respectful and appreciative of the diversity around them.

Most industrialized countries have elementary school enrollment rates of at least 90 percent. In the United States, 96 percent of children complete at least four years of elementary school. But educators in this country face a critical challenge that extends beyond enrollment: the task of educating our children to appreciate and respect diversity.

What children learn about the wide variety of people in the world around them will significantly influence the way they grow and what kind of adults them will become. It will determine whether they develop into confident, secure members of society who respect and appreciate diversity or into adults who view others with hostility and fear because of ignorance.

Understanding is the key to our acceptance of diversity. The United States is made up of hundreds of different cultures, each with different customs of speech, dress, food and behavior. Historically, this diversity has been a strength. We must teach children about the benefits of diversity.

People fear what they do not understand and this fear is often manifested as hostility. Instead of focusing their concentration on learning, young people who mistrust and fear diversity often expend their energy in unproductive anger and suspicion.

Such suspicion hurts us all. Racial and cultural stereotyping turns our homes, schools, workplaces and communities into zones of misunderstanding and mistrust. Children may grow up hearing messages that tell them members of their culture are destined to fail. If they believe these messages, they are more likely to fulfill that prophecy. Freeing young people from preconceived expectations of failure will help them avoid the pain of low self-esteem that contributes to soaring school dropout and teen pregnancy rates, violence and racial conflict, drug use and a host of other crises.

Education about our differences reduces young people's fear and replaces it with curiosity and acceptance. Helping young people to explore why others look, dress, speak and act differently can help turn their mistrust into understanding and appreciation of the rich diversity that makes up our world.

It is never to early to help children understand this diversity. Some parents, fearing that their children are too young to understand complex questions about race and culture, initially avoid the subject, hoping the discussion will be easier when the children are older.

But children who receive no information about diversity at home or school are vulnerable to the opinions expressed in a myriad of sources, including the news media, television shows, advertising, food packaging, toys and books. These influences often reinforce negative racial, cultural and sexual stereotypes. Parents and teachers should address the difficult questions about diversity before the child has a chance to be negatively influenced.

Teaching children to understand and enjoy diversity starts with defining it and describing how it is a part of all of our lives. Showing children how they have already incorporated aspects of other cultures into their own lives is one good strategy.

There are many other ways to teach children to appreciate and respect diversity. Teachers and adults can start by taking a close look at their own behavior. Each day, we have an abundance of opportunities for making a point, positive or negative, about diversity. What adults say about different foods available in the supermarket, about different neighborhoods and about what features are considered attractive in other people can have a profound influence on children.

Similarly, giving children opportunities to interact with peers from diverse backgrounds helps them to learn the differences and similarities in our culture through the bond of friendship. Sometimes, such bonds can be formed simply by being in the same classroom with children from other backgrounds. Organized activities like sports, drama or creative groups give children opportunities to share stories about themselves and their lifestyles in an informal and familiar setting.

Young people who have been successfully taught to appreciate diversity grow up to be secure adults with an understanding of other people that goes beyond the superficial attributes of skin color or accent. They are much more self-confident and capable in a variety of different situations and with many different types of people. And they are more likely to make judgments based on substantive reasons.

Teaching children about different cultures also helps them gain a deeper understanding of the way they themselves live. At a New York City elementary school, a classroom of 9- and 10-year-olds undertook an intensive, year-long study of Africa. Group work was an integral part of learning in this classroom, but individuality was concurrently emphasized. The teacher accepted that children approaching adolescence often crave conformity from their peers in dress and habits and realized that many are initially uncomfortable around those who seem different. By encouraging positive attitudes about diversity, a teacher can make sure learning takes place in an environment respectful of individuality.

The children in the New York classroom freely discussed the ways in which people who live on the African continent differ from themselves in custom, dress and eating habits. In doing so, they learned to look at their own cultures in a new light. An animated group discussion of one culture's different styles of clothing made some of the children realize how much of their own culture emphasizes clothing. A group of girls, initially horrified to learn of traditional African body-piercing, realized that ear-piercing was a form of body-piercing that they found "normal" because they were accustomed to it. And after a long group discussion in which the children argued the merits of eating raw fish, one participant showed the class a sushi menu she had been using as a bookmark.

Teachers using this curriculum say that they can see a difference in how the students respond to new reading assignments. They used to laugh or make embarrassed and inappropriate comments when they first learned of customs they found unusual. Now, they discuss the customs among themselves and compare them to their own cultures. This way of learning will have long-term benefits. The children will bring their new appreciation of differences into their adult lives, and by doing so will enjoy a talent for self-analysis possible only with the skill of comparison and the advantage of tolerance. Also, this kind of atmosphere makes the teaching process come alive for the teacher, as well as for the students.

- 1 -

Curriculums & Courses

This chapter has fully designed curriculums for multicultural education, as well as developed courses. There are courses for multicultural math, science, art, and more.

BLACK CULTURE, AFRICA, & AFRICAN-AMERICANS

African American Images, 1909 West 95th St, Chicago IL 60643. (312) 445-0322. Toll-free 1-800-552-1991. FAX (312) 445-9844. They have a comprehensive Africentric, multicultural curriculum for K-12 called SETCLAE (Self-Esteem Through Culture Leads to Academic Excellence). This curriculum has been used in over 5,000 schools. It is designed in four packages and levels. Each package includes an in-service training video, assorted books, videos, teacher's manual, a professional library, pre- and post tests, lesson plans, workbooks, SETCLAE songs and songbook, posters, awards and certificates. Prices range from $595 for basic elementary package to $995 for a complete elementary package; and $695 for basic high school package to $895 for complete high school package. Additional materials are available, such as posters ($9.95 for set of 5 outstanding African Americans); awards; workbooks; multicultural map; and songbooks.

A special home version of SETCLAE is available (without training video) for $159.95 and includes 6 children's books and 5 adult books.

Continental Press, 520 E. Bainbridge Street, Elizabethtown PA 17022. 1-800-233-0759. This company has a African American Heritage curriculum which has the readability for grades 3-4, interest level for grades 4+. The African-American history awareness program is a computer disk with files on people, events, and important data. Not only does the student learn culture, but also develops computer skills.This program consists of computer disks and a teacher's guide. Apple II, $55. Macintosh, $75. IBM/ compatibles, $55.

Emory University, African Studies Association, Credit Union Building, Atlanta GA 30322. (404) 329-6410. FAX (404) 329-6433. *African Access Review of K-12 Materials,* edited by Brenda Randolph, is a 102-page publication that includes approximately 200 signed reviews by African educators of recent print and visual materials on Africa that were produced for juvenile audiences. Spiral bound, $10.

Frank Schaeffer Publications, 23740 Hawthorne Blvd., Torrance CA 90505. (310) 378-1133. *African-Americans: Voices in History & Culture* (Proud Heritage Series), $10.95.

Golden Owl Publishing, PO Box 503, Amawalk NY 10501. (914) 962-6911. FAX (914) 962-0034. Toll-free 1-800-789-0022. Toll-free FAX 1-800-962-9101. This company has a product called JACKDAW™ which is a way to make history come alive. Each JACKDAW™ portfolio is full of primary materials, such as actual letters, diaries, telegrams, and newspaper articles. This is an innovative approach to teaching history. Prices range from $32 to $37. Order their JACKDAW™ catalog.

JACKDAWS™ about Moments in Black American history include: *Black Voting Rights*, $35; *Nat Turner's Slave Revolt*, 1831, $32.

Jamestown Publishers, PO Box 9168, Providence RI 02940. (401) 351-1915. Toll-free 1-800-USA-READ. FAX (401) 331-7257. This company specializes in reading programs.

One college level reading program is called: *Selections from the Black* (Books One through Four) edited by Edward Spargo, which contains provocative selections by Black writers. The texts are arranged to enhance vocabulary and comprehension skills.

CARIBBEAN

Continental Press, 520 E. Bainbridge Street, Elizabethtown PA 17022. 1-800-233-0759. This company has a Puerto Rico curriculum which has the readability for grades 4-5, interest level for grades 4+. The curriculum is chronologically organized from the Taínos and early Spanish explorers to contemporary issues of bilingualism and emigration. There are questions in standardized test format to focus on reading. The components are a student book, 64 pages, $6.95; teacher's guide, 4 pages, $1; and a set of 30 posters, $26.95.

JAPANESE-AMERICANS

Bess Press, PO Box 22388, Honolulu HI 96822. (808) 734-7159. FAX (808) 732-3627. This company specializes in books on Hawaii and Pacific Rim studies.

There is a curriculum for Japanese language available: *Nihongo: Introductory Japanese* by Yutaka Sato and Margaret Yamashita. This is a curriculum for high school students designed to follow the ACTFL Oral Proficiency Guidelines. Each unit includes sections on Vocabulary, Structures, Activities, Guided Conversations/ Interview, Grammar Notes, and Cultural Notes. Each lesson includes spiraling/review, expansion and elaboration of vocabulary, and grammar and tasks/functions introduced earlier. Culturally specific illustrations enhance each lesson.

JEWISH

Golden Owl Publishing, PO Box 503, Amawalk NY 10501. (914) 962-6911. FAX (914) 962-0034. Toll-free 1-800-789-0022. Toll-free FAX 1-800-962-9101. This company has a product called JACKDAW™ which is a way to make history come alive. Each JACKDAW™ portfolio is full of primary materials, such as actual letters, diaries, telegrams, and newspaper articles. This is an innovative approach to teaching history. Prices range from $32 to $37. Order their JACKDAW™ catalog.

JACKDAWS™ about Moments in Jewish history include: *The Holocaust,* $35;

NATIVE AMERICANS

Golden Owl Publishing, PO Box 503, Amawalk NY 10501. (914) 962-6911. FAX (914) 962-0034. Toll-free 1-800-789-0022. Toll-free FAX 1-800-962-9101. This company has a product called JACKDAW™ which is a way to make history come alive. Each JACKDAW™ portfolio is full of primary materials, such as actual letters, diaries, telegrams, and newspaper articles. This is an innovative approach to teaching history. Prices range from $32 to $37. Order their JACKDAW™ catalog.

JACKDAWS™ about Moments in Native American history

include: *Indian Resistance: the Patriot Chiefs,* $32.

Greenfield Review Press, PO Box 308, 2 Middle Grove Road, Greenfield Center NY 12833. (518) 583-1440. FAX (518) 583-9741. They have an entire catalog called *North American Native Authors Catalog.* This 50-page catalog contains titles on legends, history, biographies, Native women, sacred traditions, dance and ceremony, crafts and skills, education and resources, fiction, poetry, and music.

Curriculum kit for Native American experiences: *All My Relations: Sharing Native Values Through the Arts* is a looseleaf format kit to introduce Native American culture through arts, stories, and exercises. Sections keyed for grades K-6. $16.

GENERAL MULTICULTURAL

Amherst Educational Publishing, 30 Blue Hills Road, Amherst MA 01022-2220. (413) 253-7837. FAX (413) 253-7024. Toll-free 1-800-865-5549. *A Multicultural Approach to Elementary Science* by Deborah Leta Habib, for early elementary students. This material supports and values students' personal and cultural perspectives. It makes science meaningful to students in a diverse society. Each lesson includes background information, learning objectives, skills, vocabulary, and activities. $17.95.

Cultural Connections Through Art by Patricia Bode, for elementary students, shows students through art how to cherish diversity. $17.95.

Immigration to the United States: A Multicultural Social Studies Curriculum by Alice Goodwin-Brown and Trudy Teutsch, for elementary students, suggested grades 5-6. With this material, student learn to understand the immigrant experience based on the perspectives of the immigrants themselves. $17.95.

Multicultural Resource Calendar for all grade levels. This is a comprehensive resource for information and instruction about important events for over 30 different cultures. Includes a resource guide, a blackline master calendar for each month, and a bibiography. $21.95.

Center for Applied Research in Education, PO Box 430, West Nyack NY 10994. Division of Simon & Schuster. Order at: PO Box 11071, Des Moines IA 50336. Toll-free orders 1-800-947-7700. *Multicultural Discovery Activities for the Elemen-*

tary Grades by Elizabeth Stull, $27.95.

Continental Press, 520 E. Bainbridge Street, Elizabethtown PA 17022. 1-800-233-0759. This company has a general multicultural curriculum called *Communities Around the World,* for grades 3-6. Ten communities are studied, representing the hemispheric balance in terms of geography, culture, history, economics and government. Reading, writing and thinking strategies are integrated with geography, map skills, and global cultural studies. Also available in Spanish. The components are: student book, 144 pages, $7.95; teacher's edition, 168 pages $7.95. Teacher's edition includes reproducibles and world map.

Feminist Press at the City University of New York, 311 East 94th St., New York NY 10128. (212) 360-5790. FAX (212) 348-1241. This press produced the book *Women of Color and the Multicultural Curriculum: Transforming the College Classroom* edited by Liza Fiol-Matta and Mariam K. Chamberlain. This book is an actual guide that provides the tools to incorporate women of color into the curriculum across disciplines—from English literature to history, economics, sociology, and anthropology. The book documents the process of faculty development, as it actually happened at UCLA and George Washington University. It also shares the models used to educate faculty. Additionally, the book includes 37 course syllabi, and essays from professors describing their experiences teaching new texts. 400 pages, paper $18.95, cloth $35.

National Council of Teachers of Mathematics, (NCTM), 1906 Association Drive, Reston VA 22091. (703) 620-9840. Toll-free orders 1-800-235-7566. *Multicultural Mathematics: Posters & Activities* by Seattle Public Schools, Mathematics Office Staff, 64 pages, grades 7-8, $10.50. *Multicultural Mathematics Materials* by Marina C. Krause, 80 pages, grades 1-8, $8.

Tapes 'n Books for Gifted Education, 314-350 Weinacker Ave., PO Box 6448, Mobile AL 36660. Toll-free 1-800-814-1548. FAX (205) 478-4755. Formerly *The Gifted Child Today Catalog*. This company has a video called *Multicultural Dimensions of Curriculum Design* that outlines three models that should be used to develop appropriate curriculum. Video $59.97 includes printed material. Audio version $13.97; add $3 for printed material with audio.

Teacher Created Materials, Inc., 6421 Industry Way, Westminister CA 92683. (714) 891-7895. FAX (714) 892-0283. Toll-free 1-800-662-4321. *Multicultural Holidays* is a resource book providing information about more than 75 holidays along with realistic suggestions for ways to observe these holidays in classrooms. For instance, students can celebrate Black History Month (February) by making African tribal masks. The can observe Japan's Children's Day by making carp kites. All grade levels, 304 pages, $24.95.

University of Denver, Center for Teaching International Relations, Graduate School of International Studies, 2201 S. Gaylord St., Denver CO 80208. (303) 871-3106. FAX (303) 871-2456. The Center for Teaching International Relations offers courses and workshops that have teacher education concerning multicultural/ diversity studies.

Publications available to help Multicultural Awareness are: *Teaching About Cultural Awareness* by Gary Smith and George Otero, the goal of this book is to increase awareness of the diversity of ideas and practices found in human societies, with various activities, grades 4-12, comb-bound with reproducible student handouts, $24.95; *Teaching About Ethnic Heritage* by George Otero and Gary Smith, 21 activities to help students assess the role of ethnicity in their lives, designed to aid students in linking their ethnicity, identity, and heritage, grades 3-12, with reproducible handouts, $21.95; *Make a World of Difference: Creative Activities for Global Learning,* an activity book to help widen your world and that of others, all ages, $16.95.

Globalchild: Multicultural Experiences for Young Children by Maureen Ceck, is a book which shows food, clothing, dance and music resources from around the world, preschool-grade 3, $19.95. *Hand in Hand: Multicultural Experiences for Young Children* by Jacelyn Graeme and Ruth Fahlman, is a 9-book program designed to meet the need for early childhood material that positively portrays racial, cultural and linguistic diversity. Each of the nine books are written in English, French, Spanish, and Chinese, for preschool to grade 4, $78.75.

- 2 -

Textbooks, Workbooks & Supplementary Materials

This chapter has materials that are not as extensive as fully developed curriculums, but are excellent as textbooks, workbooks, or supplementary materials. There are also items such as posters, maps, and kits.

ASIAN CULTURE ASIAN-AMERICANS

Bess Press, PO Box 22388, Honolulu HI 96823. (808) 734-7159. FAX (808) 732-3627. This company specializes in books on Hawaii and Pacific Rim studies.

Asian language books by this company each contain 200 to 400 illustrated vocabulary words, a pronunciation guide and glossaries. Categories include family, home, school, the body, clothing, food, numbers, nature, and time. A cassette tape is available for each book. Languages available: Vietnamese, Korean, Filipino, Chinese, and Japanese. Prices each: paperback $11.95, hardcover $15.95, tape $7.95, book and tape $18.95.

Continental Press, 520 E. Bainbridge Street, Elizabethtown PA 17022. 1-800-233-0759. This company has a series called *Multicultural Theme Boosters* for grades 3-4, of which each set includes a trade book, a resource guide with teaching strategies and student activities as well as ideas for hands-on projects, blackline reproducibles for handouts, lists of additional resources, and a poster which is a full-color map of the region. For Japan, there is *The Stonecutter*, package $16.24. For Chinese, there is *Tye May and the Magic Brush,* $16.30.

Frank Schaeffer Publications, 23740 Hawthorne Blvd., Torrance CA 90505. (310) 378-1133. *Social Studies Resource Books* for middle grades: *Asian-Pacific Americans,* $10.95.

Friendship Press, 475 Riverside Drive, Room 772, New York NY 10115. (212) 870-2588. This company has a complete catalog with books and other resources for global living, of which there are many for multicultural education.

Map 'n Facts: Japan is a 23" x 35" full color map with information about history, geography, peoples, and religions, $4.95. *Map 'n Facts: Southern Asia* is $4.50; *Map 'n Facts: The Middle East* is $4.95; and *Map 'n Facts: The Philippines* is $4.95.

Highsmith® Inc., W5527 Highway 106, PO Box 800, Fort Atkinson, WI 53538-0800. Toll-free orders 1-800-558-2110. Toll-free customer service 1-800-558-3899. Toll-free FAX 1-800-835-2329. Highsmith is a distributor of high quality books and materials. They have a catalog called *Highsmith® Multicultural Bookstore™: Authentic Multicultural Books and Media* which has a wide selection of books for adults and children on multicultural subjects. There are children's storybooks, folktales and legends, activity books, young adult fiction and biography, literary criticism, business and finance, self help, social and political sciences, poetry, literature, culture, and much more.

Two items useful for the classroom are: *Great Asian Americans* poster set, set of 5 showing Daniel Inouye, Maxine Hong Kingston, Ellison Onizuka, I.M. Pei and Kristi Yamaguchi, $17.50; *Fun With Chinese Festivals* by Tan Huay Pens, more than 75 Chinese celebrations are brought to life on these pages in this colorful book, which includes history and heritage as well, $7.95.

Learning Works, PO Box 6187, Santa Barbara CA 93160. (805) 964-4220. Toll-free 1-800-235-5767. FAX (805) 964-1466. *The Asian Question Collection* is a book of more than 200 questions on Asian history, traditions, holidays, people, places, with answer key, grades 4-8, $7.95.

BLACK CULTURE, AFRICA & AFRICAN-AMERICAN

African American Images, 1909 West 95th St, Chicago IL 60643. (312) 445-0322. Toll-free 1-800-552-1991. FAX (312) 445-9844. *Lessons From History: A Celebration of Blackness* is a Black history textbook that goes beyond "Negro" to African history by showing its strengths, weaknesses, victories, and mistakes of African Americans. Beautifully illustrated and includes questions, exercises, and vocabulary skills. Elementary edition, grades 1-5, 108 pages, $12.95. Grades 6-Adult, 116 pages, $13.95. Teacher's Edition is free with class order.

Continental Press, 520 E. Bainbridge Street, Elizabethtown PA 17022. 1-800-233-0759. This company has a series called *Multicultural Theme Boosters* for grades 3-4, of which each set includes a trade book, a resource guide with teaching strategies and student activities as well as ideas for hands-on projects, blackline reproducibles for handouts, lists of additional resources, and a poster which is a full-color map of the region. For Africa, there is *Mufaro's Beautiful Daughters*. Package $15.20. For West Africa there is *Talk, Talk,* $15.25.

Frank Schaeffer Publications, 23740 Hawthorne Blvd., Torrance CA 90505. (310) 378-1133. Social Studies Resource Books for middle grades: *African Americans,* $10.95.

Friendship Press, 475 Riverside

Drive, Room 772, New York NY 10115. (212) 870-2588. This company has a complete catalog with books and other resources for global living, of which there are many for multicultural education.

Map 'n Facts: Africa is a 23" x 35" full color map with information about history, geography, peoples, and religions, $4.95. *Map 'n Facts: The Caribbean* is $4.95.

Highsmith® Inc., W5527 Highway 106, PO Box 800, Fort Atkinson, WI 53538-0800. Toll-free orders 1-800-558-2110. Toll-free customer service 1-800-558-3899. Toll-free FAX 1-800-835-2329. Highsmith is a distributor of high quality books and materials. They have a catalog called *Highsmith® Multicultural Bookstore™: Authentic Multicultural Books and Media* which has a wide selection of books for adults and children on multicultural subjects. There are children's storybooks, folktales and legends, activity books, young adult fiction and biography, literary criticism, business and finance, self help, social and political sciences, poetry, literature, culture, and much more.

Their catalog contains an item that is particularly useful in the classroom concerning Black culture: *Kids Explore America's African American Heritage,* written by 86 kids in grades 3 through 8, helps Black kids identify with Black culture, photos, student drawings, $9.95. Also useful are the poster sets: *African American Artists*, set of 10, $34.95; *Great Black Americans I*, set of 10, $34.95; *Great Black Americans II*, set of 10, $34.95; *Outstanding Contemporary African Americans*, set of 5, $17.50.

Identity Toys Inc., 2821 N. 4th St., Milwaukee WI 53212. (414) 562-7776. Games, puzzles, dolls and more designed with the Black child in mind.

Puzzles include *Black ABCs®* for learning the alphabet and *1-2-3 Africa®* for learning how to count to ten and to recognize the shape of Africa. Ages 3-6. $8.99 each. *Map of Africa Puzzle®* has the countries, people, wildlife and landmarks. Ages 7+, $12.99. *Legacy Puzzle®* traces the history of African Americans from early civilization to 1990s. Includes a Fact Sheet that explains the scene. Ages 10+, $14.99.

Card games include *Identity Card Game®* where children learn about the contributions of Black people through an easy to play card game. Ages 4+, $8.95. *Chocolate Kids® Flash Cards* help children develop basic learning skills such as counting, alphabet, and tracing letters and numbers. Ages 4-8, $8.

An interesting product line now available are the identity posters. There's the *African-American Child Poster,* showing a beautiful preschool Black child along with an original poem. There's also the *Legacy Poster,* that shows excerpts from Black history. Each poster $6.95.

There's also a coloring book and a calendar. *Color Me Proud®* coloring book has 50 pages to color plus 50 stickers. Ages 6+, $3. *Identity Kids® Calendar* is 12 months of African-American history, discovery, heroes, and things to do. Ages 7-12, $10.99.

Jacaranda Designs, PO Box 7936, Boulder CO 80306. (303) 440-5235. FAX (303) 440-1361. This company publishes *Authentic African Children's Books from Kenya.* These books come from the deep-rooted oral traditions of the people of Africa, which is a continent that has an enormous blending of people with strong identities.

Supplementary materials available: *Colouring Cards,* a unique set of four ready-to-color cards of African mammals, reptiles and fish. Ages 4-7, $3.95. Ages 8-11, $3.95.

Just Us Books, 301 Main St, Orange NJ 07050. (201) 672-7701. FAX (201) 677-7570. This company specializes in books and learning materials for children that focus on the African-American experience.

Learning tools for the very young African Americans include: *Afro-Bets® ABC Book, Afro-Bets® 1-2-3 Book, Afro-Bets® Book of Shapes, Afro-Bets® Book of Colors,* each for ages 2-6 about basic learning skills, 24 pages, paperback $3.95. Also available are *Afro-Bets® Coloring and Activity Book* ($3.95), *Afro-Bets® ABC Song* ($5), and *Afro-Bets® Kids Christmas Fun: A Coloring and Activity Book* ($2.95), each for ages 2-6.

Educationally oriented books for children include: *Afro-Bets® I'm Gonna Be* by Wade Hudson, where children ponder what careers they might choose when they grow up, ages 3-7, paperback, $6.95; *Afro-Bets® Book of Black Heroes from A to Z* by Wade Hudson and Valerie Wilson Wesley, "A useful item for black history collections."—*Booklist,* ages 7+, paperback, $7.95; *Book of Black Heroes: Volume II, Great Women in the Struggle* edited by Toyomi Igus, more than 80 historical and contemporary women of African descent are highlighted, ages 9+, hardcover, $17.95; paperback, $10.95; *Afro-Bets® First Book About Africa* by Veronica Freeman Ellis, "An amazing amount of information ... skillfully designed ... unparalleled."—*Booklist,* ages 3+, hardcover, $13.95, paperback $6.95.

Learning Works, PO Box 6187, Santa Barbara CA 93160. (805) 964-4220. Toll-free 1-800-235-5767. FAX (805) 964-1466. *The African Question Collection* is a book of more than 200 questions on African history, traditions, holidays, people, places, with answer key, grades 4-8, $7.95.

Third World Press, PO Box 19730, Chicago IL 60619. (312) 651-0700. FAX (312) 651-7286. They have a whole catalog of books on the black perspective. Their children's workbooks include: *The Afrocentric Self-Inventory and Discovery Workbook for African American Youth* by Useni Perkins, this workbook teaches critical thinking skills and introduces Black youth to the basics of African-centered cultural values. Ages 12-15, paper, $5.95. *A Sound Investment* by Sonia Sanchez is a classic short story collection with lessons and principles important for character development, including study/ review questions for reinforcement, making it an excellent educational tool. Grades 5-8, cloth, $18.95.

EUROPEAN CULTURE

Continental Press, 520 E. Bainbridge Street, Elizabethtown PA 17022. 1-800-233-0759. This company has a series called *Multicultural Theme Boosters* for grades 3-4, of which each set includes a trade book, a resource guide with teaching strategies and student activities as well as ideas for hands-on projects, blackline reproducibles for handouts, lists of additional resources, and a poster which is a full-color map of the region. For Italy, there is *The Mysterious Giant of Barletta,* package $15.20. For Greece, there is *The Trojan Horse,* $14.75.

Penfield Press, 215 Brown St., Iowa City IA 52245. (319) 337-9998. Toll-free 1-800-728-9998. FAX (319) 351-6846. This company "publishes books of ethnic interest and distributes books of similar interest from other publishers." There's titles about Norway, Sweden, Denmark, Finland, Iceland, Austria, Poland, Holland, Germany, Ireland, and more.

Items useful for the classroom are: *Scandinavian Boy & Girl Paper Dolls,* showing traditional folk costumes of Norway, Finland, Iceland, Sweden, Denmark and Greenland, $4.95; *Viking World,* a book with colorful pictures, maps and charts making it a very useful historical reference, 96 pages, $11.95; *Folk Costumes of the World,* with over 200 costumes from Scandinavia and Europe in color with descriptions relating each to traditions, music, dance and ritual, 256 pages, $15.95.

HISPANIC, MEXICAN SOUTH AMERICAN

Arte Público Press, The Americas Review, University of Houston, Houston TX 77204-2090. (713) 743-2998. FAX (713) 743-2847. Toll-free 1-800-633-ARTE. This is the oldest and largest publisher of Hispanic literature in the United States. Their extensive catalog includes autobiographies, fiction, poetry, drama, children's and adult literature, and more.

Useful book: *Mi primer diccionario* by Daroqui, a Spanish dictionary for children containing over 500 words, each one illustrated to help children learn the word and its spelling. Illustrated, 60 pages, hardcover, $14.95.

Another useful book for teachers and especially to libraries is: *Handbook of Hispanic Cultures of the United States* by Kanellos and Fabregat, a four-volume series on Hispanic studies that includes Volume I, Lit-

erature and Art, Volume II, History, Volume III, Sociology, Volume IV, Anthropology. Four volume set is $200.

Consortium Book Sales and Distribution, 1045 Westgate Drive, St. Paul MN 55114-1065. Toll-free orders 1-800-283-3572. FAX (612) 221-0124. This book distributor has a children's catalog full of multicultural titles.

José Rabbit's Southwest Adventures: An ABC Coloring Book with Spanish Words by Juan Alvarez introduces children to Spanish words and Southwestern culture. Ages 2-5, $3.95.

Continental Press, 520 E. Bainbridge Street, Elizabethtown PA 17022. 1-800-233-0759. This company has a series called *Multicultural Theme Boosters* for grades 3-4, of which each set includes a trade book, a resource guide with teaching strategies and student activities as well as ideas for hands-on projects, blackline reproducibles for handouts, lists of additional resources, and a poster which is a full-color map of the region. For Central America, there is *Song of the Chirimia,* package $18.20.

Friendship Press, 475 Riverside Drive, Room 772, New York NY 10115. (212) 870-2588. This company has a complete catalog with books and other resources for global living, of which there are many for multicultural education.

Map 'n Facts: Central America is a 23" x 35" full color map with information about history, geography, peoples, and religions. $4.95

Highsmith® Inc., W5527 Highway 106, PO Box 800, Fort Atkinson, WI 53538-0800. Toll-free orders 1-800-558-2110. Toll-free customer service 1-800-558-3899. Toll-free FAX 1-800-835-2329. Highsmith is a distributor of high quality books and materials. They have a catalog called *Highsmith® Multicultural Bookstore™: Authentic Multicultural Books and Media* which has a wide selection of books for adults and children on multicultural subjects. There are children's storybooks, folktales and legends, activity books, young adult fiction and biography, literary criticism, business and finance, self help, social and political sciences, poetry, literature, culture, and much more.

Two items useful for the classroom are: *My House/ Mi Casa* by Rebecca Emberly, through simple phrases young readers learn words in Spanish and English, $5.95; *Kids Explore America's Hispanic Heritage,* a book to help Hispanic children identify with their culture, photographs, drawings, written by students to help students, $9.95. Also useful are the poster sets: *Hispanic Americans Poster* set, set of 5 features Jaime Escalante, Gloria Estefan, Nancy Lopen, Manuel Lujan and Antonia Novello, $17.50; Hispanic Heritage Poster set, set of 10, $34.95.

Learning Works, PO Box 6187, Santa Barbara CA 93160. (805) 964-4220. Toll-free 1-800-235-5767. FAX (805) 964-1466. *The Hispanic Question Collection* is a book of more than 300 questions on Hispanic history, traditions, holidays, people, places, with answer key, grades 4-8, $7.95.

JEWISH CULTURE, ISRAEL

Boyds Mills Press, 815 Church St., Honesdale PA 18431. (717) 254-1164. FAX (717) 253-0179. Orders toll-free 1-800-949-7777. *Hanukkah, Happy Hannukkah: Crafts, recipes, games, puzzles, songs, and more for a joyous celebration of the Festival of Lights* by Jeff O'Hare. This book helps children understand the full story of Hannukkah, its meanings and its symbols. There are games and stories and more for educational activities. Ages 5-10, paper $4.95.

Continental Press, 520 E. Bainbridge Street, Elizabethtown PA 17022.

1-800-233-0759. This company has a series called *Multicultural Theme Boosters* for grades 3-4, of which each set includes a trade book, a resource guide with teaching strategies and student activities as well as ideas for hands-on projects, blackline reproducibles for handouts, lists of additional resources, and a poster which is a full-color map of the region. For Jewish culture, there is *It Could Always Be Worse,* package $16.20.

Learning Works, PO Box 6187, Santa Barbara CA 93160. (805) 964-4220. Toll-free 1-800-235-5767. FAX (805) 964-1466. *The Jewish Question Collection* is a book of more than 300 questions on Jewish history, traditions, holidays, people, places, with answer key, for all ages, $7.95. *The Hannukkah Happening* is a children's book filled with creative games, puzzles, recipes, facts, plenty of fun, ages 7-12, $4.95.

NATIVE AMERICAN

Chelsea House Publishers, PO Box 914, 1974 Sproul Road, Suite 400, Broomall PA 19008-0914. (610) 353-5166. Toll-free orders 1-800-362-9786. FAX (610) 359-1439. Send for the catalog called *Chelsea House Presents the Best in Indian Studies* which features *Indians of North America, the Junior Library of American Indians, North American Indians of Achievement,* a video collection, and more.

Their *Indians of North America* series provides cultural information about various tribes. Each titles offers a comprehensive profile of a particular group with photographs, paintings, maps, and a feature on Indian art and artifacts. There are 66 hardcover titles, and 23 paperback titles, including: *The Hopi; The Nez Perce; The Pueblo; The Cherokee; The Crow; The Seminole; The Navajos; the Yankton Sioux; Women in American Indian Society;* etc. Each book is 96 to 144 pages, ages 10+, hardcover $18.95, paper $7.95.

For young readers, there's the *Junior Library of American Indians.* There are over 30 titles: *The Hopi Indians; The Maya Indians; The Pueblo Indians; The Seminole Indians; The Teton Sioux Indians; The Cheyenne Indians; The Navajo Indians;* etc. Each book is 72 to 80 pages, ages 8-12, hardcover $13.95, paper $6.95.

Consortium Book Sales and Distribution, 1045 Westgate Drive, St. Paul MN 55114-1065. Toll-free orders 1-

800-283-3572. FAX (612) 221-0124. This book distributor has a children's catalog full of multicultural titles.

Chocolate, Chipmunks, and Canoes: An American Indian Words Coloring Book by Juan Alvarez. Helps children learn new words from Navajo, Hopi, Pueblo, Cree, Dakota, Inuit, and other Native American languages. Ages 2-5, $3.95.

Continental Press, 520 E. Bainbridge Street, Elizabethtown PA 17022. 1-800-233-0759. This company has a series called *Multicultural Theme Boosters* for grades 3-4, of which each set includes a trade book, a resource guide with teaching strategies and student activities as well as ideas for hands-on projects, blackline reproducibles for handouts, lists of additional resources, and a poster which is a full-color map of the region. For Native American, there is *Rainbow Crow,* package $17.24.

Franklin Watts, 95 Madison Ave., New York NY 10016. (212) 686-7070. Toll-free 1-800-621-1115. FAX 1-800-374-4329. This company has a series of *First Books* that feature illustrations, photographs, and information appropriate for children. Within this series, there are several titles on Native Americans: *The Chickasaw; The Comanches; The Hopi; The Nez Perce; The Pomo*. Each $5.95 paper.

Friendship Press, 475 Riverside Drive, Room 772, New York NY 10115. (212) 870-2588. This company has a complete catalog with books and other resources for global living, of which there are many for multicultural education.

Map 'n Facts: Native Peoples of North America is a 23" x 35" full color map with information about history, geography, peoples, and religions, $4.50.

Greenfield Review Press, PO Box 308, 2 Middle Grove Road, Greenfield Center NY 12833. (518) 583-1440. FAX (518) 583-9741. They have an entire catalog called *North American Native Authors Catalog*. This 50-page catalog contains titles on legends, history, biographies, Native women, sacred traditions, dance and ceremony, crafts and skills, education and resources, fiction, poetry, and music.

Supplemental materials include: *Dakotah Sioux Indian Dictionary* by Paul War Cloud, $6; Indian America: *A Traveler's Companion* by Eagle Walking Turtle/ Gary McClain (Choctaw) tells the reader how to find over 300 tribes, where and when visitors are welcome, what ceremonies are performed, and what arts and crafts are produced, $18.95.

Highsmith® Inc., W5527 Highway 106, PO Box 800, Fort Atkinson, WI 53538-0800. Toll-free orders 1-800-558-2110. Toll-free customer service 1-800-558-3899. Toll-free FAX 1-800-835-2329. Highsmith is a distributor of high quality books and materials. They have a catalog called *Highsmith® Multicultural Bookstore™: Authentic Multicultural Books and Media* which has a wide selection of books for adults and children on multicultural subjects. There are children's storybooks, folktales and legends, activity books, young adult fiction and biography, literary criticism, business and finance, self help, social and political sciences, poetry, literature, culture, and much more.

An items useful for the classroom is: *Native Americans Poster* set, set of 10 showing broad geographical groups of Native American cultures focusing on food, clothing, architecture, and tools, $34.95.

Middle Atlantic Press, Inc., 848 Church St., PO Box 1948, Wilmington DE 19899. *Lenape (Middle Atlantic Native American tribe) Indian Teaching Kits*. Kit #1: Introduction to the Lenape. Contains teacher's guide, Lenape numbers and symbols, posters. $22.50. Kit #2: Lenape lore, folk medicines. Contains teacher's guide, charts, quizzes. $15.50. Kit #3: Lenape lore, clothing, shelter, crafts, weapons, tools, specialties. Contains teacher's guide, charts, quizzes. $15.50.

Rand McNally Maps, PO Box 7600, Chicago IL 60680. (709) 329-8100. Toll-free 1-800-333-0134. FAX (708) 673-5136. *Discovery Atlas of Native Americans* shows where the different cultures live, $4.95, pbk.

Southwest Indian Foundation, PO Box 86, Gallup NM 87302-0001. (505) 863-4037. This nonprofit organization benefits the Indian peoples of the American Southwest. They have a catalog of interesting products, and the profits go directly back to the Indians themselves.

Their catalog includes a couple of interesting items that can be used as supplementary educational materials: *A Discovery Kit: Native Americans of the Southwest,* where children learn about Pueblo Indian cultures while excavating an Anasazi artifact. The children learn what it's like to grow up as a member of the Pueblo community. Then they are allowed to use their skills and knowledge to excavate, reassemble, and hand-paint pieces of your own Anasazi bowl replica. Ages 8+, $21. The other item is a *Native American Puzzle Set,* which is a set of four, colorful 100-piece puzzles featuring Apache, Blackfoot, Crow & Sioux tribes. Ages 5+, $17.

Tundra Books Inc., PO Box 1030, Plattsburgh NY 12901. (514) 932-5434. FAX (514) 484-2152. In U.S., orders should be sent to: University of Toronto Press, 340 Nagel Dr, Buffalo NY 14225. (716) 683-4547. FAX (416) 667-7832.

This Canadian-based publishing company has titles on Canada, China, Chinese Canadians, Native Americans, and Japanese-Canadians.

They have a *Native American Dwellings Series.* Each book is for ages 8-12, by Bonnie Shemie, covers the dwellings of a specific culture, hardcover $13.95. "A magic combination of text and image."—*The Hungry Mind Review.* "Highly useful."—*Booklist.* Titles in this series: *Mounds of Earth and Shell: The Southeast; Houses of Hide and Earth: The Plains; Houses of Bark: Woodlands; Houses of Snow, Skin and Bones: The Far North; Houses of Wood: Northwest Coast.*

GENERAL MULTICULTURAL

Consortium Book Sales and Distribution, 1045 Westgate Drive, St. Paul MN 55114-1065. Toll-free orders 1-800-283-3572. FAX (612) 221-0124. This book distributor has a children's catalog full of multicultural titles. There are more listing in the "Reading Books" chapter.

Writing Across Cultures: A Handbook on Writing Poetry & Lyrical Prose by Edna Kovac is an innovative approach—using a wide range of cultural approaches to encourage lyrical writing. Paper, $11.95.

Continental Press, 520 E. Bainbridge Street, Elizabethtown PA 17022. 1-800-233-0759. This company has *Multicultural Poster Sets* for grade 3+. Each set has 5 colorful, informative visual aids, $12.

Frank Schaeffer Publications, 23740 Hawthorne Blvd., Torrance CA 90505. (310) 378-1133. Social Studies Resource Books for middle grades: *Countries and Cultures,* $12.95, *Cultural Connections,* $12.95, *Crafts From Other Countries,* $11.95.

Garrett Park Press, PO Box 190, Garrett Park MD 20896. (301) 946-2553. Their publications *Culturegrams: The Nations Around Us* (Volume I: The Americas and Europe, Volume II: Africa, Asia and Oceania) is a series developed by the David M. Kennedy Center for International Studies at Brigham Young University. This series has been called the "best quick summary of information on the cultures and traditions of the various countries of the world." Each country has a four-page overview which includes: customary greetings, how to visit people in their homes, eating customs in the home and in restaurants, significance of certain gestures, general attitudes of the people, land and climate, history and government, educational system, state of the economy, and map of the country. The books are $75 set, or can be purchased individually for $37.50 each. Nonprofit groups receive a special price.

Gryphon House®, PO Box 275, Mt. Rainier MD 20712. Toll-free 1-800-638-0928. FAX (301) 779-6983. They have a title called *Festivals Together: A Guide to Multicultural Celebration* which is a learning tool with many creative ideas adaptable for multicultural children's celebrations and festivals throughout the year. 223 pages, paper, $19.95.

Learning Works, PO Box 6187, Santa Barbara CA 93160. (805) 964-4220. Toll-free 1-800-235-5767. FAX (805) 964-1466. Multicultural rubber stamps for decorating name tags, invitations, announcements, art. Multicultural Girls or Multicultural Boys, $5.95 each.

Celebrate! Holidays Around the World! This book provides information, activities and a coloring page on 14 holidays such as Chinese New Year, Tet, Kwanzaa, Green Corn Dance, and more. Ages 5-9, $4.95. *Holiday Art a la Carte* is a bonanza of 77 easy, illustrated ideas for holiday art projects, such as American Indian Day, United Nations Day, etc, ages 9-13, $9.95.

Stemmer House Publishers, Inc. 2627 Caves Road, Owings Mills MD 21117. (410) 363-3690. This company has a series called the *International Design Library*. These books are designs from various cultures, such as Nigerian, Aztec, Northwest Indian, Plains Indian, Peruvian textiles, Scandinavian, Chinese cut-outs, Egyptian, Japanese, etc. There's a long list of these books, each $5.95.

- 3 -

Toys & Games

Here are toys and games that are useful for a multicultural education, such as coloring books, stickers, card decks, dolls, and more.

ASIAN AMERICAN

Childcraft Education Corporation, 20 Kilmer Road, Edison NJ 08818. (908) 572-6100. This company makes multi-ethnic dolls in Hispanic, Asian, Caucasian, and Black models. Range $20-$30.

Constructive Playthings, 1227 E. 119th St, Grandview MO 64030. Toll-free 1-800-832-0572. This company makes four-piece family puppet sets, available in Asian-American.

International Playthings, 120 Riverdale Road, Riverdale NJ 07457. (201) 831-1400. They have 8" dolls available in Asian, Caucasian, or African-American, $17.95.

Pleasant Company, 8400 Fairway Place, Middleton WI 53562. Toll-free 1-800-845-0005. This company offers a soft-bodied 15" infant with vinyl head, available in Caucasian, Asian, or African-American.

BLACK CULTURE, AFRICA, & AFRICAN-AMERICANS

Aristoplay, PO Box 7028, Ann Arbor MI 48107. (313) 995-4353. Toll-free 1-800-634-7738. FAX (313) 995-4611. This company is a leader in educational toys and games—leading the way to fun learning.

Black culture: *Black History* a deck of playing cards featuring prominent black figures in the arts, human rights, science, etc. Booklet of brief biographies included. Ages 7+, $4.

Childcraft Education Corporation, 20 Kilmer Road, Edison NJ 08818. (908) 572-6100. This company makes multi-ethnic dolls in Hispanic, Asian, Caucasian, and Black models. Range $20-$30.

Constructive Playthings, 1227 E. 119th St, Grandview MO 64030. Toll-free 1-800-832-0572. This company makes four-piece family puppet sets, available in Afro-American.

Fisher Price, Inc., 636 Girar Ave., East Aurora NY 14052. (716) 687-3395. FAX (716) 687-3238. Fisher Price toys are nationally distributed and can be found in most major toys stores and department stores. Puffalump™ Dolly African-American.

Frank Schaeffer Publications, 23740 Hawthorne Blvd., Torrance CA 90505. (310) 378-1133. Bulletin board set: *Famous Black Americans,* $6.95.

Golden Ribbon, PO Box 130222, Springfield Gardens NY 11413. Toll-free 1-800-722-8285. This company won a Platinum Award from *The Best Toys, Books & Videos for Kids, 1994* for their Kwanzaa Doll, $25. The doll is dressed in traditional West African clothing, is 12", and comes either as a boy or a girl doll.

Hasbro, 1027 Newport Ave., Pawtucket RI 02861. Toll-free 1-800-752-97555. This is the parent company of Playskool®, Tonka®, Kenner®, Milton Bradley®, and Parker Brothers®. All products are nationally distributed and available in most major toy stores and department stores.

They make African-American Cabbage Patch Kids® dolls. They also have a new line called Kids of Color™ with soft infant products that celebrate cultural diversity. This line includes: Kids of Color™ Grabber Rattles, Kids of Color™ Rag Dolls, Kids of Color™ Activity Quilt, and Kids of Color™ Kente Pets.

Highsmith® Inc., W5527 Highway 106, PO Box 800, Fort Atkinson, WI 53538-0800. Toll-free orders 1-800-558-2110. Toll-free customer service 1-800-558-3899. Toll-free FAX 1-800-835-2329. Highsmith is a distributor of high quality books and materials. They have a catalog called *Highsmith® Multicultural Bookstore™: Authentic Multicultural Books and Media* which has a wide selection of books for adults and children on multicultural subjects.

There are children's storybooks, folktales and legends, activity books, young adult fiction and biography, literary criticism, business and finance, self help, social and political sciences, poetry, literature, culture, and much more.

Educational games are: *African American Bingo*, a bingo game based on identifying the contributions of 75 African Americans, $29; *Black Explorers Game* teaches math and history with each player as an explorer, $21; *In Search of Identity* an exciting way to discover black heritage, $24; *Legacy Puzzle* a historic puzzle tracing history of African Americans, $14.99; *Map of Africa Puzzle* features countries, wildlife and landmarks, $12.99; and more.

Identity Toys Inc., 2821 N. 4th St., Milwaukee WI 53212. (414) 562-7776. Games, puzzles, dolls and more designed with the Black child in mind.

In Search of Identity® board game is a way for the entire family to explore Black heritage. Each player has a secret identity and the players each try to guess the identity of the other players. Ages 8+, $24. "The Black Explorers®" board game is a math adventure game that takes each player on an exciting adventure. Ages 8-12, $21.

The Enchanting Village Game® is for young players. They explore the life of an African village. Ages 3-6, $10.99. *The Crocodile Game®* for young players has each child as a brave African warrior venturing across a dangerous river. Ages

4-8, $10.99.

Puzzles include *Black ABCs®* for learning the alphabet and *1-2-3 Africa®* for learning to count to ten and the shape of Africa. Ages 3-6, $8.99 each. *Map of Africa Puzzle®* has the countries, people, wildlife and landmarks. Ages 7+, $12.99. *Legacy Puzzle®* traces the history of African Americans from early civilization to 1990s. Includes a Fact Sheet that explains the scene. Ages 10+, $14.99.

Card games include *Identity Card Game®* where children learn about the contributions of Black people through an easy to play card game. Ages 4+, $8.95. *Chocolate Kids® Flash Cards* help children develop basic learning skills such as counting, alphabet, and tracing letters and numbers. Ages 4-8, $8.

International Playthings, 120 Riverdale Road, Riverdale NJ 07457. (201) 831-1400. They have 8" dolls available in Asian, Caucasian, or African-American, $17.95.

Learning Resources, 675 Heathrow Drive, Lincolnshire IL 60069. Toll-free 1-800-222-3909. This company has Multicultural Career Puppets, which won a Platinum Award from *The Best Toys, Books & Videos for Kids, 1994*. The puppets come in a variety of styles, including a Hispanic businesswoman, a female African-American doctor, and a Caucasian male farmer to reflect our cultural diversity in the workplace.

Little Tikes, 2180 Barlow Road, Hudson OH 44236. Toll-free 1-800-321-0183. Little Tikes Place® is a sturdy plastic dollhouse that comes with furnishings—tables, chairs, car, dog, baby, highchair, and a family of five, available in African-American.

Mattel, 333 Continental Blvd., El Segundo CA 90245. Toll-free 1-800-524-8697. They have a doll out named "Shani®" which is an African-American counterpart to Barbie™. Retails about $20.

McCall Pattern Company, 11 Penn Plaza, New York NY 10001. This company has patterns for "Heritage Dolls" which include an African-American doll. They also make patterns for Kenya™ doll and doll clothes.

Pleasant Company, 8400 Fairway Place, Middleton WI 53562. Toll-free 1-800-845-0005. This company offers a soft-bodied 15" infant with vinyl head, available in Caucasian, Asian, or African-American.

Tyco, 200 5th Ave, New York NY 10010. Toll-free 1-800-367-8926. Kenya™ is an African-American doll that comes in three skin tones and has a luxurious head of hair that can be styled various ways.

U.S. Games, 179 Ludlow St., Stamford CT 06902-6912. (203) 353-8400. *Black History Playing Card Deck*, ages 7+, $8. *Notable Black Women in American History Card Game*, $5.

EUROPEAN CULTURE

Madame Alexandra, 615 West 131st St, New York NY 10027. (212) 283-5900. This company makes 8" dolls in authentic costumes from Poland, Italy, Russia, Portugal, Ireland, and Germany, $49.95. Spanish doll $59.95.

HISPANIC, MEXICAN SOUTH AMERICAN

Aristoplay, PO Box 7028, Ann Arbor MI 48107. (313) 995-4353. Toll-free 1-800-634-7738. FAX (313) 995-4611. This company is a leader in educational toys and games—leading the way to fun learning.

Mexican learning game: *Mexican Artdeck® The Game of Modern Mexican Masters*. This game has playing cards which display the works of 13 different famous Mexican artists. Ages 10+, $5.

Childcraft Education Corporation, 20 Kilmer Road, Edison NJ 08818. (908) 572-6100. This company makes multi-ethnic dolls in Hispanic, Asian, Caucasian, and Black models. Range $20-$30.

Constructive Playthings, 1227 E. 119th St, Grandview MO 64030. Toll-free 1-800-832-0572. This company makes four-piece family puppet sets, available in Hispanic-American.

Learning Resources, 675 Heathrow Drive, Lincolnshire IL 60069. Toll-free 1-800-222-3909. This company has Multicultural Career Puppets, which won a Platinum Award from *The Best Toys, Books & Videos for Kids, 1994*. The puppets come in a variety of styles, including a Hispanic businesswoman, a female African-American doctor, and a Caucasian male farmer to reflect our cultural diversity in the workplace.

NATIVE AMERICAN

Aristoplay, PO Box 7028, Ann Arbor MI 48107. (313) 995-4353. Toll-free 1-800-634-7738. FAX (313) 995-4611. This company is a leader in educational toys and games—leading the way to fun learning.

Native American educational game: *A Time for Native Americans* with jumbo-size playing cards about prominent Native Americans in history. Ages 10+, $5.

Frank Schaeffer Publications, 23740 Hawthorne Blvd., Torrance CA 90505. (310) 378-1133. Bulletin board set: *North American Indians,* $6.95.

McCall Pattern Company, 11 Penn Plaza, New York NY 10001. This company has patterns for "Heritage Dolls," which include one for a Native American doll.

Patail, 27324 Camino Capistrano #129, Laguna Niguel CA 92677. (714) 367-0530. This company makes an *Eskimo Art Kit* where the child can make a hunter in a kayak, a whale and a mythological ten-legged bear. Kit includes everything needed for these items plus detailed instructions, $20. Ages 9+.

U.S. Games, 179 Ludlow St., Stamford CT 06902-6912. (203) 353-8400. FAX (203) 353-8431. Toll-free orders 1-800-544-2637. *Native American Playing Cards, Deck I and II,* each $7.

GENERAL MULTICULTURAL

Aristoplay, PO Box 7028, Ann Arbor MI 48107. (313) 995-4353. Toll-free 1-800-634-7738. FAX (313) 995-4611. This company is a leader in educational toys and games—leading the way to fun learning. *Friends Around the World®* is a game of world peace that teaches the benefits and fun of cooperation. This game introduces children to cultures of other lands. Ages 5+, $10.

Fisher Price, Inc., 636 Girar Ave., East Aurora NY 14052. (716) 687-3395. FAX (716) 687-3238. Fisher Price toys are nationally distributed and can be found in most major toys stores and department stores. They have a new series of toys from The Puzzle Place™ which is a new daily PBS series for young children. This series helps teach kids to appreciate differences through "puppet kids" from diverse backgrounds. The toys that accompany this series are: The Puzzle Place™ My Friend™ Dolls, for ages 2+, soft-bodied huggable dolls (six dolls in all: Mexican-American, Jewish, African-American, Norwegian-American, Native American—Apache, and Chinese American); *Let's Make a Puzzle Game,* cooperative game for ages 3+; *Memory Game,* ages 3+; *On My Own Reader*, an electronic reader for ages 3+, and *Mini Playsets* to teach kids what it's like to live in different parts of the country, such as a farm in South Dakota or homes in Manhattan, Arizona, San Antonio, San Francisco, etc.

Frank Schaeffer Publications, 23740 Hawthorne Blvd., Torrance CA 90505. (310) 378-1133. *A World of Friends Floor Puzzle,* 24 large pieces, for ages 3+, $12.95. Chart [poster] *Greetings Around the World,* for how to say "Hello" in different places in the world, $1.50.

Friendship Press, 475 Riverside Drive, Room 772, New York NY 10115. (212) 870-2588. *A World of Children's Games* edited by Mary Duckert, 192 pages, hardcover, $19.95. This book has more than 100 games from around the world, located by continent. Each games notes how many players, the ages of the participants, equipment required, easy-to-follow rules plus an explanation of the purpose or history behind the game.

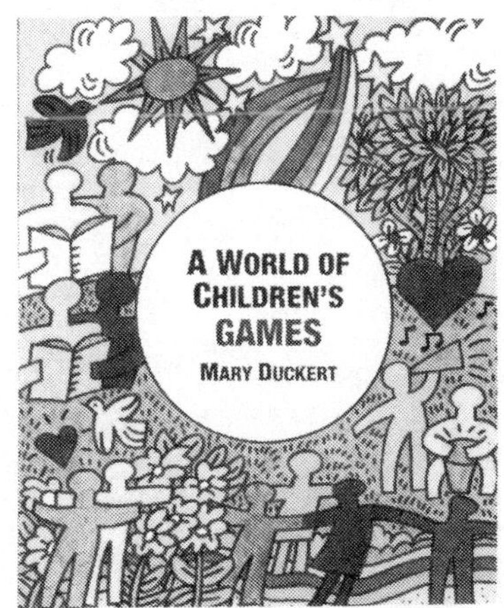

- 4 -

Software & Computers

This chapter has software and computer courses for multicultural education. This field will be growing rapidly in the next few years.

BLACK CULTURE, AFRICA & AFRICAN-AMERICANS

Continental Press, 520 E. Bainbridge Street, Elizabethtown PA 17022. 1-800-233-0759. This company has a African American Heritage curriculum with the readability for grades 3-4, interest level for grades 4+. The African-American history awareness program is a computer disk with files on people, events, and important data. Not only does the student learn about culture, but also develops computer skills. This program consists of computer disks and a teacher's guide. Apple II, $55. Macintosh, $75. IBM/compatibles, $55.

HISPANIC CULTURE

Learning Company, 6493 Kaiser Drive, Fremont CA 94555. (510) 792-2101. *Bilingual Writing Center* lets the student work in Spanish or English, and teaches the student to write reports. Macintosh, $229.

Children's Writing and Publishing Center is also in Spanish/English and is a student desktop publishing software. Grades 205, IBM compatible, $99.95.

Mind*Play*, 160 West Ft. Lowell, Tucson AZ 85705. (520) 888-1800. FAX (520) 888-7904. Toll-free orders 1-800-221-7911. This company has bilingual educational software. *Carrera Contra el Tiempo*™/*Race the Clock*™ bilingual Macintosh version, displays a verb on the screen as actions and lets students match words, grade Pre K-adult. *Fraccion-Oides*™/ *Fraction-*

Oids™ (versions I, II, or III), bilingual Macintosh version, explores fraction terms, provides practice with fractions, 15 levels of difficulty. *La Calle Sin Problemas*™ / *Easy Street*™ bilingual MS-DOS and Macintosh versions, for reading, math and problem-solving skills, grades Pre K-3. Call for price information.

Ventura Educational Systems, Creative Teacher Division, 910 Ramona Avenue, Suite E, Grover Beach CA 93433-2154. Toll-free orders 1-800-336-1022. This company has some bilingual software. Their preschool and early grades software includes: *Storybook Weaver Spanish* is a creative tool that kids can use to write and illustrate their own stories. Grades Pre K-4, Macintosh, $55.95; *Stickybear's Bilingual Reading Room* is a new reading and thinking skills program with four learning activities in two languages, English and Spanish, Pre K-3, Macintosh or IBM, single $34.95, school $45.95; *Stickybear's Early Learning Activities* is a program with graphics and clear speech in English and Spanish, Pre K-1, Macintosh or IBM, single $34.95, school $45.95.

Elementary level software: the ever popular *Where in the World is Carmen Sandiego* is now in Spanish—*Donde esta Carmen Sandiego?*, Winner of the Best Learning Product Award from the Software Publisher Association, grades 5+, Macintosh or IBM, $69.95; *The Bilingual Writing Center* lets teachers and students create a wide array of documents with full color graphics and text, grades 2+, Macintosh, school $159.95, lab $389.95; *Language Explorer (Nordic)* lets the student select a topic and a language, then place the correct tiles in the correct frames—an easy way to learn French, English, Spanish and German, grades K-adult, Macintosh or IBM, single $32.95, lab $131.95; *Kid Works 2 Bilingual* allows children to create and illustrate their own stories in English or Spanish, grades K-5, Macintosh or IBM, school $111.95, lab $239.95.

GENERAL MULTICULTURAL

Broderbund Software, PO Box 6125, Novato CA 94948-6125. Toll-free orders 1-800-521-6263. *Living Books* has interactive stories in English, Spanish, and some Japanese, which teaches the alphabet, sciences, songs, and more. Comes for ages 3-8 or 6-10, $39.95 each.

Electronic Courseware Systems, Inc., 1210 Lancaster Drive, Champaign IL 61821. (217) 359-7099. FAX (217) 359-6578. Toll-free orders 1-800-832-4965. They have available *Dr. T's Sing-a-long Around the World* which was developed with input from educators, parents, and kids themselves. This software is a children's musical theater, with colorful, warm animations to give kids a window on the world of music and fun. Includes a songbook with lyrics for all songs. Ages 3-10. IBM compatible, $39.95.

Another product of interest in a multicultural education is *Microsoft Musical Instruments* which brings more than 200 instruments from around the world to life. All the student needs to do is click the mouse to learn how an instrument works, hear musical examples, or listen to jazz, classical, rock, or other ensembles play. It is simple to use, yet captivating. IBM Windows or Macintosh, $79.95.

Ventura Educational Systems, Creative Teacher Division, 910 Ramona Avenue, Suite E, Grover Beach CA 93433-2154. Toll-free orders 1-800-336-1022. Elementary level software: *Language Explorer (Nordic)* lets the student select a topic and a language, then place the correct tiles in the correct frames—an easy way to learn French, English, Spanish and German, grades K-adult, Macintosh or IBM, single $32.95, lab $131.95.

- 5 -

Reading Books

There are many great reading books for multicultural education. This is one area which has had an explosion of publishing in the last few years. Following this chapter is a section called: "Hot Picks," which is the editor's choice of favorite books .

ASIAN CULTURE AND ASIAN-AMERICANS (Japanese Culture has its own section)

Atheneum, 866 3rd Ave., New York NY 10022. (212) 702-2000.Sh-Ko wants to court Yakami, but he can't because of his obligations. Instead, his eight wicked brothers court her, but she is not fooled. *Sh-Ko and His Eight Wicked Brothers* by Ashley Bryan is a Japanese tale of humor and entertainment. Ages 4-8, $12.98.

Boyds Mills Press, 815 Church St., Honesdale PA 18431. (717) 254-1164. FAX (717) 253-0179. Orders toll-free 1-800-949-7777. Chinese-American title in their catalog: *First Apple* by Ching Yeung Russell, is an autobiographical novel set in the 1940s which tells of the author's youth in China and her dream to buy her grandmother a special birthday gift—an apple, which is rare in her part of China. Ages 7-10, hardcover, $13.95.

Calyx, PO Box B, Corvallis OR 97339. (503) 753-9384. FAX (503) 753-0515. This publisher exists to nurture women's creativity through the publication and wide promotion of women's finest artistic and literary work. Some of their titles are excellent multicultural resources.

Asian titles: *Black Candle: Poems about Women from India, Pakistan, and Bangladesh* by Chitra Divakaruni, with a bicultural perspective, shows the pain and the joys of South Asian women, $9.95; *Ginseng and Other Tales from Manila* by Marianne Villanueva, stories from the Philippines that show new insights into human nature and the courage of these people, $8.95; *The Forbidden Stitch: An Asian American Women's Anthology* shows the experience of being an "Asian American woman," the diversities and the similarities, [and, quite frankly, one of the most beautiful and unique book covers ever printed] $32.

Chelsea House Publishers, PO Box 914, 1974 Sproul Road, Suite 400, Broomall PA 19008-0914. (610) 353-5166. Toll-free orders 1-800-362-9786. FAX (610) 359-1439. *Ancient China* is a lively look at this past civilization with detailed illustrations, photographs, which look at the clothing, food, family life, and religion. It includes a traditional story and activities that can be performed at home. Also *The Mongols,* same format. Ages 8-12, grade 3-7, paper $7.95.

They have a series called The Asian American experience with titles such as: *Spacious Dreams: The First Wave of Asian Immigration; Journey to Gold Mountains: The Chinese in Nineteenth Century America; Raising Cane: The World of Plantation Hawaii; Issei and Nissei: The Settling of Japanese America; Ethnic Islands: The Emergence of Urban Chinese America; From the Land of Morning Calm: The Koreans in America.* Each book 128 pages, all ages, hardcover $18.95.

Children's Book Press, 6400 Hollis St., Suite 4, Emeryville CA 94608. (510) 655-3395. FAX (510) 655-1978. Multicultural titles for children about African-American, Hispanic, Asian-American, Jewish American, and Native American subjects.

Chinese American title: *China's Bravest Girl* by Charlie Chin, about a daughter who decides she must go to war because there is no eldest son. Ages 6-12, $13.95, bilingual in English and Chinese. Vietnamese American title: *The Little Weaver of Thai-Yen Village* by Tran-Khan-Tuyet, about a Vietnamese girl adjusting to her new life in the United States. Ages 7-12, $13.95, bilingual in English and Vietnamese.

Laotian title: *Nine-In-One, Grr! Grr!* by Blia Xiong, a Laotian folk tale. Ages 4-10, $13.95, in English. Cambodian title: *Judge Rabbit and the Tree Spirit* by Lina Mao Wall, about a Cambodian folk hero. Ages 6-12, $13.95, bilingual in English and Khmer.

Children's Press®, 5440 North Cumberland Ave., Chicago IL 60656-1494. Toll-free 1-800-621-1115. FAX 1-800-374-4329. This publisher has an extensive line of fine books for kids, and there are many good multicultural titles.

Their Asian titles include biographies: *Bette Bao Lord: Novelist and Chinese Voice for Change, Dr. An Wang: Computer Pioneer, Nien Cheng: Courage in China,* each $5.95.

Another children's reading title is: *Kao and the Golden Fish by Cheryl Hamada,* hardcover, $12.95, paper, $5.95.

Consortium Book Sales and Distribution, 1045 Westgate Drive, St. Paul MN 55114-1065. Toll-free orders 1-800-283-3572. FAX (612) 221-0124. This book distributor has a children's catalog full of multicultural titles.

Who Belongs Here? An American Story by Margy Burns Knights won an award for Best Multicultural Title, 1993 Publishers Weekly Off-the-Cuff Awards. Based on the story of Nary, a young Cambodian immigrant, this picture book asks pertinent questions about racism and political activism. Showing Nary's experiences with name-calling and harassment, the author makes children think about who really "belongs" in this country. Ages 5+, hardcover, $16.95.

Essential Learning Products, 2300 West Fifth Avenue, PO Box 2590, Columbus OH 43216-2590. (614) 486-0633. FAX (614) 487-2272. *The Whispering Cloth* is about a Laotian refuge exiled in Thailand, ages 3-8, hardcover $14.95.

Highsmith® Inc., W5527 Highway 106, PO Box 800, Fort Atkinson, WI 53538-0800. Toll-free orders 1-800-558-2110. Toll-free customer service 1-800-558-3899. Toll-free FAX 1-800-835-2329. Highsmith is a distributor of high quality books and materials. They have a catalog called *Highsmith® Multicultural Bookstore™: Authentic Multicultural Books and Media* which has a wide selection of books for adults and children on multicultural subjects. There are children's storybooks, folktales and legends, activity books, young adult fiction and biography, literary criticism, business and finance, self help, social and political sciences, poetry, literature, culture, and much more.

Their Asian American titles include some children favorites such as: *The Korean Cinderella* by Shirley

Climo, a story of Pearl Blossom who is treated like a slave by her stepmother, $15; *The Seven Chinese Brothers* by Margaret Mahy, the classic folktale, $13.95; *The Blue Jackal* by Rashmi Sharma, an East Indian tale shows the value of people in a multiracial society is not based on color, $14.95.

Holiday House, Inc., 425 Madison Ave., New York NY 10017. They have a catalog of children's books.

The Girl Who Wanted to Hunt: A Siberian Tale describes the adventures of little Anga, who lives in a hut by the Amur River, in the great forest of Siberia. She wants to be a hunter like her father, but her stepmother says that hunting is not girl's work. Ages 4-8, 32 pages, $15.95.

Macmillan Publishing Company, Inc., 866 3rd Ave., 25th Floor, New York NY 10022. (212) 702-2000. Toll-free orders 1-800-257-5755. A Chinese girl in San Francisco who does all the work while her shiftless brother take the credit, that's the story of *Roses Sing on New Snow* by Paul Yee. Ages 6+, $13.95.

Museum of New Mexico Press, PO Box 2087, Santa Fe NM 87504. (505) 827-6454. FAX (505) 827-7308. This press has a lot of books about the Southwest, its Indian population, and the Hispanic influence. There are books about Pueblo Indians, Navajos, and New Mexican art and culture.

One book on East Indian culture is: *Mud, Mirror, and Thread: Folk Traditions of Rural India,* which shows items from a world-class collection of rural Indian textiles, pottery, ornamentation, and folk decorations, 256 pages, 175 color plates, clothbound $60, paperbound, $45.

Temple University Press, Broad and Oxford Sts., Philadelphia PA 19122. (215) 204-8787. Toll-free 1-800-447-1656. FAX (215) 204-4719. Their catalog includes sections on Ethnic Studies, African American Studies, Asian American Studies, and Latino Studies.

Their Asian Studies titles include: *Making Ethnic Choices: California's Punjab Mexican Americans* by Karen Isaksen Leonard, which describes how men from India's Punjab district came to California to work on the land. These men married women of Mexican descent. The book shows how group perceptions of ethnic identity have changed, 352 pages, paper $18.95, cloth $49.95. *Asian American Panethnicity: Bridg-*

ing Institutions and Identities by Yen Le Espiritu, shows how Americans of Chinese, Japanese, Filipino, Korean and Vietnamese origins are lumped together and viewed by Americans simply as Asians, 240 pages, paper $16.95, cloth $34.95.

Tundra Books Inc., PO Box 1030, Plattsburgh NY 12901. (514) 932-5434. FAX (514) 484-2152. In U.S., orders should be sent to: University of Toronto Press, 340 Nagel Dr, Buffalo NY 14225. (716) 683-4547. FAX (416) 667-7832.

This Canadian-based publishing company has titles on Canada, China, Chinese Canadians, Native Americans, and Japanese-Canadians.

Five Heavenly Emperors describes 12 Chinese creation myths by author Song Nan Zhang. Ages 8+, hardcover, $17.95.

A Little Tiger in the Chinese Night is an autobiography in art by Song Nan Zhang. This book won a 1994 Mr. Christie's Book Award. "Unusually immediate and authentic."—*Kirkus Reviews*. "The writing is so vivid and the story so involving that it is hard to put down ... A book that beautifully fulfills its writer's intentions and widens its readers' horizons."—*Booklist*. 48 pages, hardcover $19.95.

West Coast Chinese Boy by Sing Lim is about this boy's childhood in Vancouver's Chinatown in the 1920's. 64 pages, ages 10+, paper $7.95.

BLACK CULTURE AFRICAN-AMERICANS & AFRICA

A & B Distributors, Inc., 11-25 Brandford Place, Store #25B, Newark NJ 07102. Tel/ FAX: (201) 824-2556. Other location: 149 Lawrence St., Brooklyn NY 11201. (718) 596-3389. FAX (718) 596-0968. This company publishes and distributes Afro-American literature and products for children and adults. Some educational books include: *Afro-Tots ABC*, $3.95; *Afro-Tots Numbers 1-2-3*, $3.95; *When I Look in the Mirror,* a self esteem book, $5.95; *Little Zeng* for teaching African history, $4.95.

Abrams, 100 Fifth Avenue, New York NY 10011. Sales office (212) 206-7715. Customer service (201) 387-0600. Toll-free orders only 1-800-345-1359. FAX (212) 645-8437.They have a list of books on African and African-American art and artists. Titles include: *Black Art: Ancestral Legacy: The African Impulse in African-American Art,* "Will long be the definitive word on the subject."—*Library Journal,* 320 illustrations with 170 in full color, 304 pages, $49.50; *Harlem Renaissance: Art of Black America*, "The artists spotlighted here powerfully convey a black American identity through visual images when from memory, history, experience,"—*Publishers Weekly*, 140 illustrations, 200 pages, $14.98; *African Ark: People and Ancient Cultures of Ethiopia and the Horn of Africa*, "The photographs are stupendous, radiating the energy of lives ordered by tradition and strong cultural identities,"—*Booklist*, 300 illustrations, 240 in full color, 320 pages, $65.

African American Images, 1909 West 95th St, Chicago IL 60643. (312) 445-0322. Toll-free 1-800-552-1991. FAX (312) 445-9844. This company has a catalog containing numerous books useful for a multicultural education program, including black fairy tales, comics, Black history, African geography and history, biographies, sociological and psychological topics including Black women's issues, books about racism and its effects, motivational titles, and more.

Some educational books for children include: *A is for Africa*, a preschool book with beautiful illustrations, $5.95; *Africa is Not a Country, It's a Continent* (grades 4-8), $9.95; *Afro-Bets First Book About Africa* (grades 2-5), $6.95; *Malcolm X* (grades 2-5), $5.95.

Biographies of Black Americans include: Duke Ellington, Frederick Douglass, Ben Carson, Malcolm X, Martin Luther King, Jr., Nat Turner, Paul Roberson, Sojourner Truth, Thurgood Marshall, Jackie Robinson, and more.

Africa World Press, 11-D Princess Road, Lawrenceville NJ 08648. (609) 844-9583. FAX (609) 844-0198. This company specializes in books on black Americans, everything from their African history to present black culture. There are books for adults as well as children. Examples of their adult titles: *Malcolm X as Cultural Hero and other Afrocentric Essays* by Molefi Kete Aante, cloth $39.95, paper, $12.95; *Long Hammering: Essays on the Forging of an African-American Presence in the Hudson River Valley to the Early Twentieth Century* by A.J. Williams-Myers, cloth, $45.95, paper $14.95; *Too Much Schooling, Too Little Education: A Paradox of Black Life in White Societies* edited by Mwalimu J. Shajaa, cloth $45.95, paper $16.95.

There are titles on African civilization, apartheid in South Africa and other places, black people in the Old West, Caribbean culture, black women in literature, books of African names, and much more.

There's titles for young people as well: *A is for Africa, Looking at African through the Alphabet,* hardcover, $12.95; *The Black Creators*, Volumes I and II, hardcover $16.95, paper, $8.95 each; *The Black Inventors*, Volumes I and II, hardcover $16.95, paper, $8.95 each; *Glorious Age in Africa: The Story of Three Great African Empires,* hardcover $19.95, paper $7.95; *The Days When the Animals Talked: Black American Folktales & How They Came To Be*, hardcover, $29.95, paper, $12.95.

You really need to see the entire catalog to make your selections from these excellent books.

Albert Whitman & Company, 6340 Oakton St., Morton Grove IL 60053-2723. (708) 581-0033. Toll-free 1-800-255-7675. FAX (708) 581-0039. *The Gifts of Kwanzaa* by Synthis Saint James, shows a joyous celebration of this holiday. Ages 3-7, 32 pgs, hardcover, $14.95.

Alfred A. Knopf, Inc., 201 E. 50th St., New York NY 10022. (212) 572-2103. Toll-free 1-800-733-3000. Twenty-four tales including animal tales, tall tales, supernatural tales, and more are in *The People Could Fly: American Black Folktales* by Virginia Hamilton. Ages 6+, $12.95.

Black Classic Press, PO Box 13414, Baltimore MD 21203-3414. Orders toll-free 1-800-476-8870. Their recent title *A Time of Terror* by James Cameron, has been featured on *Good Morning America, CBS Sunday Morning, Larry King Live,* in *Newsweek, The Washington Post,* and more. This is the true account of what happened to James Cameron back in 1930, when he was nearly lynched by a mob in Marion, Indiana. This chilling tale is a reminder of America's terrifying past. Cameron has also opened the only museum of its kind in Milwaukee, America's Black Holocaust Museum, inspired by Jerusalem's Jewish Holocaust Museum. The author originally self-published this book in 1982, and it has been reissued by Black Classic Press. 207 pages, cloth $22, paper $14.95.

Other titles of interest include: *African People in World History* by John Henrik Clarke, sets the record straight about African history and shows the significant people and events that shaped African, African-

American and world history, paper, $8.95; *African Life and Customs* by Edward W. Blyden, a reissue of a 1908 collection of articles that examines the social and economic structure of African society at the turn of the century, paper, $8.95; *50 Plus Essential Reference on the History of African People* by Asa Hilliard III, a bibliography which answers the questions such as: Who are the African people? Where did they come from? What is the state of African people today? 24 pages, $3; *Black Geneology* by Charles Blockson is a complete and practical guidebook for tracing black family history, cloth $24.95, paper $14.95.

Send for full catalog and their newsletter.

Boyds Mills Press, 815 Church St., Honesdale PA 18431. (717) 254-1164. FAX (717) 253-0179. Orders toll-free 1-800-949-7777. Their African-American title is: *Families: Poems Celebrating the African American Experience* selected by Dorothy Strickland and Michael Strickland. This book explores family relationships and the diversity of the African American family. Ages 5-8, hardcover, $14.95.

Calyx, PO Box B, Corvallis OR 97339. (503) 753-9384. FAX (503) 753-0515. This publisher strives to nurture women's creativity through the publication and wide promotion of women's finest artistic and literary work. Some of their titles are excellent multicultural resources.

An African American title: *Killing Color* by Charlotte Watson Sherman. These are village stories that move beyond the ordinary to the otherworldly with a mythical quality which explores the African American experience, paper $9.95, cloth $19.95.

Chelsea House Publishers, PO Box 914, 1974 Sproul Road, Suite 400, Broomall PA 19008-0914. (610) 353-5166. Toll-free orders 1-800-362-9786. FAX (610) 359-1439. Send for the catalog called *Chelsea House Presents the Best in Black Studies* which features Black American history, profiles of great Black Americans, Black music, video collection, and more.

They have a series of books showing milestones in black American history, such as: *From the Framing of the Constitution to Walker's Appeal; From the Emancipation Proclamation to the Civil Rights Bill; From the Sounding of Southern Christian Leadership Conference to the*

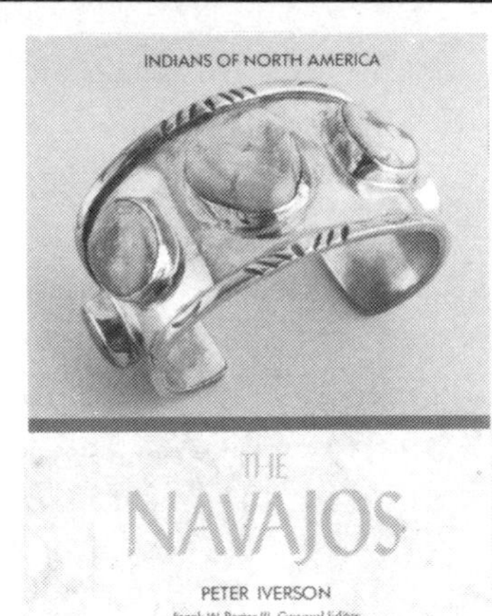

Chelsea House has numerous publications in many ethnic areas, so be sure to send for their catalog. *Chelsea House Publishers*, 1-800-362-9786

Assassination of Malcolm X; etc. Each book is 128 to 144 pages, ages 10+, hardcover $18.95, paper $7.95. Another series profiles great Black Americans: *Book of Firsts: Leaders of America; Civil Rights Leaders; Female Leaders; Performing Artists; Pioneers of Discovery,* etc. Each book is 64 pages, ages 8+, hardcover $13.95, paper $5.95.

Another series is *Black Americans of Achievement: Dizzy Gillespie; Whoopi Goldberg; Spike Lee; Michael Jackson; Michael Jordan; Oprah Winfrey; James Baldwin; Muhammed Ali; Ella Fitzgerald; Barbara Jordan; Malcolm X;* etc. There are over 100 titles in this series, and it is targeted for young adults. Each book is 104 to 144 pages, hardcover $18.95, paper $7.95.

For junior readers, there's a series called *Junior Black Americans of Achievement: George Washington Carver; Magic Johnson; Malcolm X; Thurgood Marshall; Madam C.J. Walker,* etc. Each book is 72 to 80 pages, hardcover $14.95, paper $4.95.

Children's Book Press, 6400 Hollis St., Suite 4, Emeryville CA 94608. (510) 655-3395. FAX (510) 655-1978. Multicultural titles for children about African-American, Hispanic, Asian-American, Jewish American, and Native American subjects.

African American titles: *I Remember "121"* by Francine

Haskins, celebrates the joys of growing up in a traditional African American family. Ages 4-12, $13.95. *The Barber's Cutting Edge* by Gwendolyn Battle-Lavert, about the friendly barber who passes on his love of language and respect for learning. Ages 6-12, $14.95. *Things I Like About Grandma* by Francine Haskins. About "the value and importance of the extended family"—*Multicultural Review.* Ages 4-10, $13.95.

Children's Press®, 5440 North Cumberland Ave., Chicago IL 60656-1494. Toll-free 1-800-621-1115. FAX 1-800-374-4329. This publisher has an extensive line of fine books for kids, and there are many good multicultural titles.

Extraordinary Black Americans from Colonial to Contemporary Times is a collection of short, easy-to-read biographies and historical events to acquaint children with the extraordinary accomplishments of black Americans. Grade 6+, 208 pages, $15.95.

Many Voices, One Song is a rhyming story that tells the story of many courageous African-Americans who followed their dreams to create a better life—not only for themselves but for others as well. Ages 4-9, 48 pages, $6.95.

They have a holiday books, *Kwanzaa* and *Martin Luther King Day,* each $3.95. There are biographies, *Booker T. Washington, Malcolm X, Mary McLeod Bethune,* and more, each $3.95

Clarion Books, 215 Park Ave South, New York NY 10009. (212) 420-5800. Stories from West Africa's Trinidad have been collected in *A Wave in Her Pocket: Stories from Trinindad* by Lynn Joseph. Some of the tales are chilling, some are humorous, but all are entertaining. Ages 8+, $13.95.

Consortium Book Sales and Distribution, 1045 Westgate Drive, St. Paul MN 55114-1065. Toll-free orders 1-800-283-3572. FAX (612) 221-0124. This book distributor has a children's catalog full of multicultural titles.

Journey Toward Freedom: The Story of Sojourner Truth by Jacqueline Bernard is the biography of an African-American woman. "A magnificent biography of a magnificent woman, told with no strident blare of trumpets, but with a steady roll of drums."—*Publishers Weekly.* Young adults, ages 10+, hardcover $35, paper $12.95.

Council Oak Books, 1350 East 15th

St., Tulsa OK 74120. (918) 587-6454. FAX (918) 583-4995. *The Last Train North* by Clifton L. Taulbert, is an account of his 1963 migration from the Mississippi Delta to St. Louis, $9.95.

Crown Publishing Group, 201 E. 50th St., New York NY 10022. (212) 751-2600. Toll-free orders 1-800-726-0600. *Tar Beach* by Faith Ringgold is a fantasy with Cassie Lightfoot of Harlem wearing the lights of George Washington Bridge like a diamond necklace. Ages 5+, $14.95.

Dial, 375 Hudson St., New York NY 10014. (212) 366-2000. December 1, 1965 is a day that is famous in civil rights history. It is the day that a very weary Rosa Parks refused to give up her bus seat in Montgomery, Alabama. *Rosa Parks: My Story* is her autobiography, written for ages 10+, $17.

Duke University Press, Box 90660, Durham NC 27708-0660. (919) 687-3600. Orders (919) 688-5134. FAX (919) 688-4574. They publish *Within the Circle: An Anthology of African American Literary Criticism from the Harlem Renaissance to the Present*, edited by Angelyn Mitchell. This is the first anthology to present the entire spectrum of 20th century African American literary and cultural criticism. The essays in this collection gave critical definition to specific periods or movements of African American literature. 584 pages, paper $18.95, library cloth edition, $49.95.

Eschar Publications, PO Box 1196, Waynesboro VA 22980. They are the publishers of *Nadandam, The Wordmaker* by Vivian Owens. Ms. Owens listened to the stories of her grandmothers and her great-grandmother as she grew up in Florida. Their stories inspired her to create her own. In this story, fourteen-year-old Nadanda creates words no one has ever heard of. She is a wordmaker. This makes her popular with other kids, but unfortunately, she doesn't feel accepted by her mother. One day her mother brings home an ancient African doll, which leads them on an adventure that shows that Nadanda's made-up words do have meaning after all. Hardcover, $16.95.

Friendship Press, 475 Riverside Drive, Room 772, New York NY 10115. (212) 870-2588. This company has a complete catalog with books and other resources for global living, of which there are many for multicultural education.

Born of the Sun: A Namibian Novel by Joseph Diescho is the story of a young black Namibian pressured to work the mines, separated from his new wife, and struggling against apartheid. "A book rich in history and culture."—*New York Times Book Review*. $6.95.

Franklin Watts, 95 Madison Ave., New York NY 10016. (212) 686-7070. Toll-free 1-800-621-1115. FAX 1-800-374-4329. *Historic Speeches of African Americans* by Warren Halliburton, inspiring speeches by great African Americans such as Fredrick Douglass, Martin Luther King, Jr., Malcolm X, Shirley Chisholm, Jesse Jackson, and more. $6.95 paper. *The Negro Leagues: The Story of Black Baseball* by Jacob Margolies, tells about when Black people had their own baseball league. $6.95 paper.

HarperCollins, 10 E. 53rd St., New York NY 10022. (212) 207-7000. Toll-free 1-800-331-3761. *Brown Angels* by Walter Myers shows early 20th century photographs of African-American children accompanied by poetry. Ages 6+, $16.

Harvard University Press, 79 Garden St, Cambridge MA 02138. Toll-free 1-800-448-2242. (617) 495-2480. FAX toll-free 1-800-962-4983. *The Black Columbiad: Defining Moments in African American Literature and Culture* edited by Werner Sollors and Maria Diedrich. Distinguished scholars, critics, and writers from around the world gather in this book to examine a great variety of moments that have defined the African American experience. This landmark text in African American studies reveals the often unpredictable variety of complex forces that have been at work in black America. 416 pages, hardcover $39.95; paper $16.95.

Highsmith® Inc., W5527 Highway 106, PO Box 800, Fort Atkinson, WI 53538-0800. Toll-free orders 1-800-558-2110. Toll-free customer service 1-800-558-3899. Toll-free FAX 1-800-835-2329. Highsmith is a distributor of high quality books and materials. They have a catalog called *Highsmith® Multicultural Bookstore™: Authentic Multicultural Books and Media* which has a wide selection of books for adults and children on multicultural subjects. There are children's storybooks, folktales and legends, activity books, young adult fiction and biography, literary criticism, business and fi-

nance, self help, social and political sciences, poetry, literature, culture, and much more.

There are numerous books on Black culture from various publishers. Many of the most popular multicultural titles are found in this catalog, such as: *Afro-Bets® Series, Great African American Series Sets, Biographies of Outstanding Black American Series,* the series *A Documentary History of the Negro People in the U.S.*, and much, much more.

A very useful item for librarians and teachers is *Children & Books I: African American Storybooks and Activities for All Children,* with reviews of 86 books, $14.95. Send for the catalog to see all the titles.

Holiday House, Inc., 425 Madison Ave., New York NY 10017. They have a catalog of children's books.

The Singing Man is a story adapted from a West African folktale about three brothers, one of who is a musician. The other brothers objected, saying Banzar should do something useful for the village or leave. This is the story of how Banzar realizes his dreams. Ages 4-8, 36 pages, $14.95.

There is also a holiday book, *Celebrating Kwanzaa,* $6.95.

Holloway House Publishing Co., 8060 Melrose Ave., Los Angeles CA 90046-7082. (213) 653-8060. FAX (213) 655-9452. Publisher of Black experience paperbacks. They have a new *Black Americans Series* of titles: *Thurgood Marshall* by Joe Nazel, about the first Black Supreme Court justice; *Elijah Muhammed* by Malu Halasa, about the man who built the Nation of Islam into a major religious and social force in the African-American community, $3.95; *Madam C.J. Walker* by Cookie Lommel, about the first self-made black female millionaire in the U.S.; *Paul Laurence Dunbar* by Tony Gentry, about the first major African-American poet; *Count Basie* by Bud Liment, about the bandleader and musician; *Mary McLeod Bethune* by Bernice Anderson Poole, about the leading African-American educator; more titles. Each book $3.95.

Inland Book Company, PO Box 120261, East Haven Ct 06512. (203) 467-4257. FAX 1-800-334-3892. *From Swing to Soul: An Illustrated History of African American Popular Music from 1930 to 1960,* traces the sounds of African American influence and innovation in mid-20th century music, with biographies and photos of major personalties. Hardcover, $32.50. *From Cakewalks to Concert Halls: An Illustrated History of African American Popular Music from 1895 to 1930*, a prize-winning book that traces the growth of this form of music from blackface minstrelsy to the big band era. Hardcover, $32.50, paper $21.95.

Jacaranda Designs, PO Box 7936, Boulder CO 80306. (303) 440-5235. FAX (303) 440-1361.This company publishes *Authentic African Children's Books from Kenya.* These books come from the deep-rooted oral traditions of the people of Africa, which is a continent that has an enormous blending of people with strong identities.

The Secret of the Mango Grove is a new book on the African environmental perspective. This is the story of a young girl and her efforts to help her father understand the delicate balance of life in his mango grove. Ages 4-8, 24 pages, paper, $4.95. *Beneath the Rainbow: A Collection of Children's Stories and poems from Kenya,* Volumes I, ages 7-10, 48 pages, paper, $9.95; Volume II, ages 7-10, 80 pages, paper $14.95.

John Muir Publications, PO Box 613, Santa Fe NM 87504. (505) 982-4078. FAX (505) 988-1680. Toll-free 1-800-285-4078. This company has a new series of books called *Kids Explore* ... which has been drawing acclaim by experts for its content and format. These books are written for kids by kids, (the students in the Westridge Young Writers Workshop in Littleton, Colorado) and explore the diversity of American culture. Each book is 7" x 9", 112 to 144 pages, $9.95. This has been said about *Kids Explore America's African American Heritage*: "[K]ids and grown-ups, too, will find this enjoyable reading all year round."—*L.A. Parent*. "The most interesting aspect of the book ... [is] the authors—the students who did the actual reports."—*Booklist*.

Jossey-Bass Inc., Publishers, c/o Macmillan Publishing Group, 100 Front St, Box 500, Riverside NJ 08075-7500. Toll-free 1-800-257-5755. FAX toll-free 1-800-562-1272. Publishers of the book *The Dreamkeepers: Successful Teachers of African American Children* by Gloria Ladson-Billings. This author draws on her own educational experience as an African American student, teacher, and parent to highlight a handful of individuals and programs that are turning dreams into reality. She shows eight teachers whose style and methods are strengthening cultural identity. 200 pages, cloth, $22.

Just Us Books, 301 Main St, Orange NJ 07050. (201) 672-7701. FAX (201) 677-7570. This company specializes in books and learning materials for children that focus on the African-American experience.

There is a series of books for junior high school students. Book #1 is *Neate to the Rescue* by Debbi Chocolate, where Naimah helps her mom's city council reelection. "It's good to see a school-teen series with an African-American cast; it's also good to see series teens involved in political action."—*Bulletin of the Center for Children's Books*. Ages 10+, paperback, $3.95. Book #2 is *Elizabeth's Wish* by Debbi Chocolate, with the Neate group of junior high school students and their second exciting adventure, ages 10+, paperback $3.95.

Other storybooks include *Land of the Four Winds* by Veronica Freeman Ellis, about a boy named Tonieh who is transported by winds to a far off land, an exciting fantasy that combines elements of West African folklore, contemporary Liberian dialect, and African oral tradition. Ages 6-9, hardcover $14.95, paperback $6.95. Also *Annie's Gifts* by Angela Medearis. Annie has a talented musical family. But Annie is not musically inclined. Finally, Annie learns that her gifts are important too. Ages 7-11, hardcover, $14.95, paperback, $6.95.

Educationally oriented books for children include: *Afro-Bets® I'm Gonna Be* by Wade Hudson, where children ponder what careers they might choose when they grow up, ages 3-7, paperback, $6.95; *Afro-Bets® Book of Black Heroes from A to Z* by Wade Hudson and Valerie Wilson Wesley, "A useful item for black history collections."—*Booklist,* ages 7+, paperback, $7.95; *Book of Black Heroes: Volume II, Great Women in the Struggle* edited by Toyomi Igus. More than 80 historical and contemporary women of African descent are highlighted, ages 9+, hardcover, $17.95; paperback, $10.95; *Afro-Bets® First Book About Africa* by Veronica Freeman Ellis, "An amazing amount of information ... skillfully designed ... unparalleled."—*Booklist,* ages 3+, hardcover, $13.95, paperback $6.95.

Lathrop, Lee & Shephard Books, 1350 Avenue of the Americas, New York NY 10019. (212) 261-6500. Toll-free 1-800-843-9389. *Mufaro's Beautiful Daughters,* by award-winning children's writer John Steptoe, was inspired by a folktale in Zimbabwe. This tale is about two beautiful daughters, one of which is very spoiled. The king wants a wife, and Mufaro wants him to choose between his two beautiful daughters, but the spoiled one, Manyara, doesn't want to leave this to chance, and thus the tale progresses.

Lee & Low Books, 228 East 45th Street, New York NY 10017. (212) 867-6155. FAX (212) 338-9059. This company produces award-winning multicultural titles for young readers. Their commitment to authenticity includes having authors working in cooperation with many outside resources to create their titles. Their titles include books about black culture, Japanese-American culture, and Hispanic culture.

Children's titles on black culture include: *Joshua's Masaii Mask* by Dakari Hru, "Its message is splendidly universal ... in ways that should engage any American child."—*New York Times,* "A story centering on real children with real feelings."—*Publishers Weekly*, ages 3-10, hardcover $14.95; *Saturday at the New You* by Barbara E. Barber, an African American girl uses her imagination to help deal with a difficult customer in her mother's beauty salon, ages 3-8, hardcover, $14.95; *Zora Hurston and the Chinaberry Tree* by

William Miller, is a true story about the famous African American writer, who as a young girl, learned about hope and strength from her mother, ages 4+, hardcover, $14.95; *Bein' With You This Way* by W. Nikola-Lisa, a playground rap that introduces young readers to how people are different yet the same, a book for parents and teachers to use as an introduction to racial and physical differences, "A wonderful recommendation for young children,"—*American Bookseller*, Children's Book-of-the-Month Club Selection, ages 2-8, hardcover, $14.95.

Louisiana State University Press, PO Box 25053, Baton Rouge LA 70894-5053. (504) 388-8271. FAX (504) 388-6461. This university press has a list of African-American Studies titles that includes a variety of themes, such as: *Ethiopianism and Afro-Americans in Southern Africa,* $32.50; *History of Afro-American Literature*, Vol I, $29.95; *Telling Memories Among Southern Women*, $24.95. There are quite a few studies of African American slavery, such as *Rise and Fall of Black Slavery,* $14.95; *Slavery Attacked*, $39.95; *South and the Politics of Slavery*, $9.95. Send for their list of African-American titles.

Minnesota Historical Society Press, 345 Kellogg Blvd. West, St. Paul MN 55102-1906. (612) 296-7539. Toll-free orders 1-800-647-7827. FAX (612) 297-1345. This press has multicultural studies about Native American tribes (Sioux, Ojibway [Chippewa], Hidatsa), African American, Scandinavian, and Hispanic.

African American studies titles: *Days of Rhondo* by Evelyn Fairbanks is an affectionate memoir of growing up during the 30's and 40's in St. Paul's largest Black neighborhood, 182 pages, $12.95. Also available on audio book, read by the author, 2 cassettes, $16.95. *Black Minnesotans*, a reprint of an issue of *Roots* magazine exploring the origins and development of the present-day black community in the Twin Cities, ages 12+, 44 pages, $3.50; *Blacks in Minnesota: A Preliminary Guide to Historical Sources,* 33 pages, $3.

Morrow, 1350 Avenue of the Americas, New York NY 10019. (212) 261-6691. From the land of the some of the world's mightiest warriors comes *Shaka, King of the Zulus* by Diane Stanley and Peter Vennema. This is the biography of a man who, as a child was an outcast. He eventually became a courageous and mighty warrior. Ages 7-12, $13.95.

National Archives, Trust Fund Boards, Washington DC 20408. Toll-free 1-800-788-6282. FAX (301) 763-6025. *Black History: A Guide to Civilian Records in the National Archives* compiled by Debra Newman, is an award-winning research guide providing accurate, concise information about civilian records held by the National Archives. These records can be used to study the history of African Americans, 379 pages, hardcover $25, paper $15.

Open Hand Publishing, Inc., PO Box 22048, Seattle WA 98122-0048. (206) 323-2187. FAX (206) 323-2188.

Pathblazers: Eight People Who Made a Difference by M.K. Fullen, is about eight African Americans who contributed to civil rights, education, and the arts: Septima Clark, Jester Hairston, Josephine Baker, Thurgood Marshall, Gwendolyn Brooks, James Forman, Andrew Young, and Barbara Jordan, 64 pages, paper $6.95, cloth $12.95. *Sylvia Stark: A Pioneer* by Victoria Scott and Ernest Jones, is the true story of an African American Pioneer. Sylvia was freed from slavery at the age of 12 and traveled the Oregon Trail by covered wagon to California. 64 pages, paper $6.95, cloth $12.95. *Black Heroes of the Wild West* by Ruth Pelz, shows the black presence on the frontier. 58 pages, paper $6.95, cloth $12.95.

Pelican Publishing Company, PO Box 3110, Gretna, LA 70054. (504) 368-1175 customer service. FAX (504) 368-1195. Ordering toll-free 1-800-843-1724. *Olympic Black Women* by Martha Ward Plowden, highlights the accomplishments of African American women, who have been competing in the Olympics since 1932, $16.95. *Clementine Hunter: American Folk Artist,* $42.95; *Famous Firsts of Black Americans,* $11.95; *Famous Firsts of Black Women,* $15.95. Children's African American titles: *D.J. and the Zulu Parade,* $14.95; *A Good Soup Attracts Chairs: A First African Cookbook for American Kids,* $18.95.

Peter Bedrick Books, 2112 Broadway, Room 318, New York NY 10023. (212) 496-0751. Distributed by Publishers Group West, toll-free 1-800-788-3123. *Two Tickets to Freedom: The True Story of Ellen & William Craft, Fugitive Slaves* by popular award-winning children's author J. Ezra Keats. Grades 4+, $12.95, paperback $5.95.

Red Sea Press, Inc., 11-D Princess Road, Lawrenceville NJ 08648. (609) 844-9583. FAX (609) 844-0198. This company specializes in books about the horn of Africa. Some of their titles are: *The Oromo of Ethiopia: A History,* by Mohammed Hassen, cloth $49.95, paper, $16.95; *Emergent Eritrea: Challenges of Economic Development* by Gebre Hiwet Tesfagiorgis, cloth $45.95, paper, $16.95; *Ethiopia and Eritrea: A Documentary Study* compiled by Habtu Ghebre-Ab, cloth $45.95, paper $16.95. Send for their catalog of titles.

Scholastic Inc., 555 Broadway, New York NY 10012. (212) 343-6100. Toll-free orders 1-800-325-6149. *Happy Birthday, Martin Luther King* by Jean Mazollo is a book that tells very young children what Dr. King wanted to change in America. Ages 307, $14.95. *Learning to Swim in Swaziland* by Nila Leigh, shows 8-year-old Nila, who has just moved to Swaziland, writing letters to her friends in New York. It portrays traveling from the point of view of a youngster. Ages 5-8, $15.95.

Temple University Press, Broad and Oxford Sts., Philadelphia PA 19122. (215) 204-8787. Toll-free 1-800-447-1656. FAX (215) 204-4719. Their catalog includes scholarly books on Ethnic Studies, African American Studies, Asian American Studies, and Latino Studies.

Their African American Studies titles include: *African American Reflections on Brazil's Racial Paradise,* which shows how reports in the early 20th century of Brazil as the utopia for people of color were affirmed by notable black observers until the middle of the century; $34.95. *The Children of Strangers: The Stories of a Black Family* by Kathryn Morgan. Based on the collections from her own family's stories and photographs, she portrays five generations of black women and their attempts to cope with the fears and anxieties of life in a white society, $12.95.

Third World Press, PO Box 19730, Chicago IL 60619. (312) 651-0700. FAX (312) 651-7286. They have a whole catalog of books on the black perspective. Their children's books include: *The Afrocentric Self-Inventory and Discovery Workbook for African American Youth* by Useni Perkins. This workbook teaches critical thinking skills and introduces Black youth to the basics of African-centered cultural values. Ages 12-15, paper, $5.95. *A Sound Investment* by

Sonia Sanchez is a classic short story collection with lessons and principles important for character development. It includes study/ review questions for reinforcement, making it an excellent educational tool. Grades 5-8, cloth, $18.95. *Children of Africa: A Coloring Book* introduces African American children to their African origins. Paper, $5.95.

University of Illinois Press, 1325 South Oak St., Champaign IL 61820. Toll-free 1-800-545-4703. This publisher has an extensive list of books on Black Studies. It includes many detailed and scholarly studies on African-American history and culture.

University Press of Mississippi, 3825 Ridgewood Road, Jackson MS 39211-6492. (601) 982-6272. Toll-free 1-800-737-7788. FAX (601) 982-6217. This press has a large selection of African American heritage books, including: *The Civil Rights Movement in America,* which is a compilation of papers presented at the 11th annual Porter L. Fortune Chancellor's Symposium on Southern History held at the University of Mississippi in 1985, 188 pages, cloth $27.50, paper $14.95; *The Fruits of Integration: Black Middle-Class Ideology and Culture, 1960-1990,* by Charles Banner-Haley, shows how black middle-class culture has had an impact on mainstream America, 288 pages, cloth $40, paper $16.95; and biographies on Booker T. Washington and Margaret Walker.

Viking Penguin, 375 Hudson St., New York NY 10014. (212) 366-2000. Toll-free 1-800-331-4624. Award-winning *Golden Bear* by Ruth Young is a story of a small African-American child and his teddy bear. Preschool-grade 1, $14. Another popular title is *The Snowy Day* by J. Ezra Keats, who is a popular award-winning children's author. Preschool-grade 1, $13.

Winston-Derek Publishers Group Inc., PO Box 90883, Nashville TN 37209. Toll-free 1-800-826-1888 or 1-800-225-2256. FAX (615) 329-4824. This company has a large selection of African American titles. Their topics include titles about Christianity and blacks, African American education, cookbooks, and more.

Examples of African American-Christian titles found in their catalog are: *The Original African Heritage Study Bible,* which is an authorized King James version that contains verses about African Biblical characters, leatherette $44.50, bonded leather $59.95, genuine leather $79.95; *Bible-Legacy of the Black Race; The Prophecy Fulfilled* by Joyce Andrews, explores what the Bible says regarding this complicated issue, paper, $11.95; *Did God Make Them Black?* by Isaac O. Olaleye, explores the varied beliefs for racial differences through biblical references and scientific research, hardcover, $14.95; *100 Amazing Facts on the African Presence in the Bible*, from biblical customs to characters in familiar Bible stories, this book contains a wealth of information for the reader, paper, $5.95.

Titles about African American education: *Issues in African American Education* by Walter Gill, Ph.D., is a collection of essays that point the way to radical changes in our educational system in response to the needs of the African American population, paper $8.95; *Afro American Encyclopedia* is the first encyclopedia published about African Americans. Published 30 years after the Civil War, it contains addresses, lectures, vital statistics, education, business, and is a valuable historical reference, paper, $24.95; *The Miseducation of the Negro* by Carter G. Woodson, first published in 1933 by this educator who has been called the "Father of Negro History," these concepts are still valid today, paper, $7.95.

CANADIAN CULTURE

Tundra Books Inc., PO Box 1030, Plattsburgh NY 12901. (514) 932-5434. FAX (514) 484-2152. In U.S., orders should be sent to: University of Toronto Press, 340 Nagel Dr, Buffalo NY 14225. (716) 683-4547. FAX (416) 667-7832.

This Canadian-based publishing company has titles on Canada, China, Chinese Canadians, Native Americans, and Japanese-Canadians.

West Coast Chinese Boy by Sing Lim is about this boy's childhood in Vancouver's Chinatown in the 1920's. 64 pages, ages 10+, paper $7.95.

The Montreal of My Childhood by Antonio de Thomasis shows Montreal in the 1950's. All ages, hardcover, $22.95.

CARIBBEAN CULTURE

Boyds Mills Press, 815 Church St., Honesdale PA 18431. (717) 254-1164. FAX (717) 253-0179. Orders toll-free 1-800-949-7777. Caribbean title in their catalog: *Caribbean*

Canvas: Reflections from the West Indies illustrated by Frané Lessac, is a collection of beautiful poems by well-known West Indies poets such as Evan Jones, Susan Wallace, Edward Brathwaite, etc. She also includes some original West Indian proverbs, such as "You live in de cement house, and no worry de hurricane." All ages, 24 pages, hardcover $15.95.

Friendship Press, 475 Riverside Drive, Room 772, New York NY 10115. (212) 870-2588. This company has a complete catalog with books and other resources for global living, of which there are many for multicultural education.

Choices and other stories from the Caribbean have 7 stories of moments of decision and other significant turning points in the lives of children in Cuba, Haiti, St. Vincent, Guyana and Jamaica, $6.95.

Lift Every Voice, Multicultural and Minority Source Materials Company, 16 Park Lane, Newton Centre MA 02159-1731. (617) 244-9808. FAX (617) 964-5432. This company has a *Children and Adult Multicultural Book Tape and Video Catalog*. Two very useful books are *Guide to the 400 Best Children's Multicultural Books* ($35) and *Guide to Children's Multicultural Books of the Caribbean* ($7).

EUROPEAN CULTURE

Alfred A. Knopf, Inc., 201 E. 50th St., New York NY 10022. (212) 572-2103. Toll-free 1-800-733-3000. *Klara's New World* by Jeanette Winter is the story of a Swedish girl moving to America with her family. Ages 5-8, $15.

Chelsea House Publishers, PO Box 914, 1974 Sproul Road, Suite 400, Broomall PA 19008-0914. (610) 353-5166. Toll-free orders 1-800-362-9786. FAX (610) 359-1439. *The Vikings* is a lively look at this past civilization with detailed illustrations, photographs, and a look at the clothing, food, family life, and religion. It includes a traditional story and activities that can be performed at home. Also *The Romans* and *Ancient Greece,* same format. Ages 8-12, grades 3-7, paper $7.95.

Longstreet Press, 2140 Newmarket Parkway, Suite 118, Marietta GA 30067. (404) 980-1488. Toll-free 1-800-927-1488. FAX (404) 859-9894. Their titles to introduce children to European culture are: *If I Lived in*

France and *If I Lived in Spain,* each by Rosanne Knorr and illustrated by John Knorr. Each book shows the daily lives of children in that country—their schooling, their outdoor activities, their cultural experience, and some introductory words of the language. Each book is $14.95 hardcover, 40 pages.

Minnesota Historical Society Press, 345 Kellogg Blvd. West, St. Paul MN 55102-1906. (612) 296-7539. Toll-free orders 1-800-647-7827. FAX (612) 297-1345. This press has multicultural studies about Native American tribes (Sioux, Ojibway [Chippewa], Hidatsa), African American, Scandinavian, and Hispanic.

Scandinavian titles include: *The Emigrants* by Johan Bojer, 351 pages, $12.95; *The Minnesota Ethnic Food Book* by Anne Kaplan, 449 pages, $14.95.

Northland Publishing, PO Box 1389, 2900 N. Fort Valley Road, Flagstaff, AZ 86001. (602) 774-5251. Toll-free 1-800-346-3257. FAX (602) 774-0592. *The Lost Norwegian: Recipes from Scandinavia and Beyond* by Christin Drake, 208 pages, $19.95.

Pelican Publishing Company, PO Box 3110, Gretna, LA 70054. (504) 368-1175 customer service. FAX (504) 368-1195. Ordering toll-free 1-800-843-1724. *An Irish Night Before Christmas* by Sarah Kirwan Blazek, tells how Christmas is a little different around the Emerald Isle—humorously, of course. 32 pages, $14.95.

Penfield Press, 215 Brown St., Iowa City IA 52245. (319) 337-9998. Toll-free 1-800-728-9998. FAX (319) 351-6846. This company "publishes books of ethnic interest and distributes book of similar interest from other publishers." There's titles about Norway, Sweden, Denmark, Finland, Iceland, Austria, Poland, Holland, Germany, Ireland, and more.

As soon as I opened their catalog, I ordered copies of *Norwegian Proverbs* for my Norwegian friends. I was delighted! This book, $10.95, has material selected from the tales of Peter Christian Asbjornsen and Jorgen Moe. There's also some pictures of beautiful Norwegian antiques. So I expect that readers would be equally as thrilled with *Danish Proverbs* or *Swedish Proverbs*, each $10.95. Other Scandinavian titles include: *Proverbs from the North: Words of Wisdom from the Vikings* translated from the Icelandic by Noanne Asala, 64 pages, $10.95; *Trolls Remembering Norway: Sto-*

ries and History by Joanne Asala, a book not to be missed by fans of this legendary character, $12.95; *Swedish Folktales and Legends* edited by Lone Thygesen Blecher and George Blecher, 448 pages, $25.

Other Northern European titles include: *People in the Summer Night,* a Finnish tale originally published in 1934, $16.95; *Mogens and Other Stories,* a collection of Danish stories, $13.95; *The Moon Man,* a Polish adventure story by an artist who has won many awards, $15.95.

The title that originally brought my attention to this company is *The New German Cookbook,* with more than 230 contemporary and traditional recipes, 416 pages, $25.

Shambhala, c/o Random House, Inc., 400 Hahn Road, Westminister MD 21157. Toll-free 1-800-733-3000. In Hawaii, Alaska & Maryland, call toll-free 1-800-492-0782. Publishes the title *Salt is Sweeter than Gold* by Andrew Peters, about the famous Czech folktale that was the inspiration for Shakespeare's King Lear. Children's book, 32 pages, hardcover $16.

Stemmer House Publishers, Inc. 2627 Caves Road, Owings Mills MD 21117. (410) 363-3690. They publish the book *The Magic Storysinger: From the Finnish Epic Kalevala* retold and illustrated by M.E.A. McNeil. This book tells about the adventures of the great mythic Finnish hero Vaino. Humor, adventure, and magic abound in this classic tale about the legendary hero who accomplished great feats. Hardcover, 144 pages, illustrated, $16.95.

HAWAIIAN CULTURE

Bess Press, PO Box 22388, Honolulu HI 96823. (808) 734-7159. FAX (808) 732-3627. This company specializes in books on Hawaii and Pacific Rim studies.

Hawaiian books for children include: *Where's Kim?* by Jeff Langcaon, a hidden-picture book where guide Kimo and his tour group visit 10 visitor attractions on the islands, 24 pages, $5.95; *Whose Slippers Are Those?* by Marilyn Kahalweai, for ages 2-5, for teaching children colors, sizes, and opposites by comparing and contrasting something familiar to Hawaiian children: slippers, 16 pages, $7.95; *Maui Mouse's Supper* by Marilyn Kahalewai, a story of a hungry mouse and her adventures, 16 pages, $5.95; *Talking Story with Nona Beamer,* a collection of 12 Hawaiian tales of yesteryear, 80 pages, $9.95.

There's also Hawaiian language books: *Learn Hawaii at Home* by Kahikahealani Wight, a self study program using a book and two cassette tapes, $29.95; *Hawaiian Word Book,* with 200 words illustrated and presented with various aspects of Hawaiian culture, paper $11.95, hardcover, $15.95, cassette tape $7.95.

Hawaiian history and culture is provided in: *Hawaii: Our Island State,* long a standard classroom text for Hawaiian history, 421 pages, $25.95; *The Hawaiians of Old,* shows the detail and complexity of ancient Hawaiian culture, 229 pages, $27.95, workbook, 88 pages, $6.95, teacher's manual $6.95; *Hawaii: The Aloha State,* covers Hawaiian history from ancient times through statehood to the present, 192 pages, $27.95, workbook, 72 pages, $6.95, answer key, $6.95.

Booklines Hawaii, 94-527 Puahi St, Waipahu HI 96797. (808) 676-0116. FAX (808) 676-0634. This company specializes in books on Hawaiian and Hawaiian culture. For a look at Hawaiian history, try *Hawaiian Journey* by Joseph Mullins, now in its 8th printing, traces Hawaii's colorful history in words and pictures, $11.95. For a look at the relationship of the Hawaiian people to the land, in context with ancient Hawaiian religious, philosophical and environmental thought, there's the book *Man Gods and Nature* by Kioni Dudley, $12.95.

Chelsea House Publishers, PO Box 914, 1974 Sproul Road, Suite 400, Broomall PA 19008-0914. (610) 353-5166. Toll-free orders 1-800-362-9786. FAX (610) 359-1439. *Raising Cane: The World of Plantation Hawaii,* 128 pages, all ages, hardcover $18.95.

HISPANIC, MEXICAN, AND SOUTH AMERICAN CULTURE

Arte Público Press, The Americas Review, University of Houston, Houston TX 77204-2090. (713) 743-2998. FAX (713) 743-2847. Toll-free 1-800-633-ARTE. This is the oldest and largest publisher of Hispanic literature in the United States. Their extensive catalog includes autobiographies, fiction, poetry, drama, children's and adult literature, and more.

Children's books of interest: *El tesoro de los cuentos,* a collection of classic stories, such as The Emperor's New Clothes, Tom Thumb, and more, translated into Spanish, hardcover, $15.95; *En mundo encan-*

tado, again a translation of classics, such as Grimm's and Anderson's fairy tales, hardcover, $15.95.

An interesting autobiography for young adults is *Barrio Teacher* by Arcadia López. It details this woman's development from a childhood of immigration and poverty, to her lifelong achievement of becoming a teacher in the barrio. 96 pages, $9.50.

Carolrhoda, 241 1st Ave N., Minneapolis MN 55401. (612) 332-3344. The Guatemalan legend of the chirimia, a musical pipe, is the background of the love story in *Song of the Chirimia/La Música de la Chirimia* by Jane Anne Volkmer. Ages 5+, $12.95.

Chelsea House Publishers, PO Box 914, 1974 Sproul Road, Suite 400, Broomall PA 19008-0914. (610) 353-5166. Toll-free orders 1-800-362-9786. FAX (610) 359-1439. *The Maya* is a lively look at this past civilization with detailed illustrations, photographs, and a look at the clothing, food, family life, and religion. Includes a traditional story and activities that can be performed at home. They also have *The Aztecs*, same format. Ages 8-12, grade 3-7, paper, $7.95.

They have a series called Hispanics of Achievement which focus on the lives and accomplishments of prominent Hispanic men and women, such as: *Julio César Chávez; Joan Baez; Plácido Domingo; Gloria Estefan; Rita Morena; Diego Rivera*; and more. Each book $7.95, paperback.

Another series is Junior Hispanics of Achievement, designed for young readers: *Robert Clemente; Gloria Estefan; César Chávez*. Each $4.95, paperback.

Children's Book Press, 6400 Hollis St., Suite 4, Emeryville CA 94608. (510) 655-3395. FAX (510) 655-1978. Multicultural titles for children about African-American, Hispanic, Asian-American, Jewish American, and Native American subjects.

Mexican culture titles include: *Angel's Kite* by Alberto Blanco, about a young kitemaker who brings back the missing bell of his town. Ages 6-12, $13.95, bilingual in Spanish and English. *The Desert Mermaid* by Alberto Blanco, a contemporary folktale about the ecology of the desert. Ages 5-12, $13.95, bilingual in Spanish and English.

Winner of a Texas Bluebonnet Award and ALA Notable Book is *Family Pictures/Cuadros de Familia* by Carmen Lomas Garza, with memories of childhood that are "an inspired celebration of American cultural diversity."—*School Library Journal*. Ages 6-12, $13.95.

Puerto Rico titles: *Atariba and Niguayona* by Harriet Rohmer and Jesus Guerrero Rea. "The moving story of the young boy's quest for the tall caimoni tree whose fruit will save the life of the ailing Atariba."—*Booklist*. Ages 6-12, $13.95. *My Aunt Otilia's Spirits* by Richard Garcia, about the aunt who comes to visit and brings her "noisy spirits" with her. Ages 6-12, $13.95.

Nicaragua titles: *Mother Scorpion Country* by Harriet Rohmer and Dorminister Wilson, "the story of a young Miskito Indian who accompanies his wife, Kati, to Mother Scorpion Country, which is beyond the land of the living."—*San Francisco Chronicle*. Ages 8-12, $13.95. (Bilingual cassette also available at $9.95.)

Children's Press®, 5440 North Cumberland Ave., Chicago IL 60656-1494. Toll-free 1-800-621-1115. FAX 1-800-374-4329. This publisher has an extensive line of fine books for kids, and there are many good multicultural titles.

Their Hispanic titles include picture-story biographies for ages 7-10: *Carolina Herrera: International Fashion Designer, César Chávez and La Causa, Evelyn Cisneros: Prima Ballerina, Everett Alvarez, Jr.: A Hero for Our Times,* and more, each $3.95. They also have a holiday book, *Cinco de Mayo*, $3.95.

Consortium Book Sales and Distribution, 1045 Westgate Drive, St. Paul MN 55114-1065. Toll-free orders 1-800-283-3572. FAX (612) 221-0124. This book distributor has a children's catalog full of multicultural titles.

Where the Cinnamon Winds Blow (Done soplan los vientos de canela) by Jim Sagel is an English/Spanish bilingual fantasy rooted in the cultural context of the Hispanic Southwest and tells about the adventures of Tomás in his search for maturity and self realization. Ages 10-14, paper $12.95.

My Mother the Mail Carrier/ Mi Mama la Cartera by Inex Maury shows five-year-old Lupita and her mother, who loves not only her child, but her job. Ages 4-9, paper $7.95.

José Rabbit's Southwest Adventures: An ABC Coloring Book with Spanish Words by Juan Alvarex introduces children to Spanish words and Southwestern culture. Ages 2-5, $3.95.

DDL Books, Inc., 6521 NW 87th Avenue, Miami FL 33178. Toll-free orders 1-800-635-4276. FAX (305) 477-5632. This distributor has a catalog *Spanish Children's Literature Catalog*.

Some of the bestsellers available in Spanish are: *Canciones y Poemas para Niños* by Federico Garcia-Lorca, now in its 17th edition. It is a book of lyrical pieces that evokes the sounds of Spain, paper $4.95; *El Tapiz del Abuela* by Omar Castañeda, the award-winning tale of Esperanza and her grandmother, hardcover $14.95, paper $5.95; *Una Grieta en la Pared* by Mary Elizabeth Haggerty, about Carlos and his mother in their new but dingy apartment, where Carlos uses his imagination to create something beautiful out of ugly cracks in the wall, hardcover, $14.95, paper, $5.95.

There are many more titles available in this catalog, such as dual-language books, and books in Spanish such as: the Barbar series, the Indiana Jones collection, fairy tales, novels, classics (*Gulliver's Travels, Ivanhoe, Treasure Island*, etc.), science experiments, religious books, dictionaries, atlases, and more.

Essential Learning Products, 2300 West Fifth Avenue, PO Box 2590, Columbus OH 43216-2590. (614) 486-0633. FAX (614) 487-2272. *Amazon: A Young Reader's Look at the Last Frontier* shows a cultural depiction of Rondonia, grades 4-6, hardcover $17.95.

Highsmith® Inc., W5527 Highway 106, PO Box 800, Fort Atkinson, WI 53538-0800. Toll-free orders 1-800-

558-2110. Toll-free customer service 1-800-558-3899. Toll-free FAX 1-800-835-2329. Highsmith is a distributor of high quality books and materials. They have a catalog called *Highsmith® Multicultural Bookstore™: Authentic Multicultural Books and Media* which has a wide selection of books for adults and children on multicultural subjects. There are children's storybooks, folktales and legends, activity books, young adult fiction and biography, literary criticism, business and finance, self help, social and political sciences, poetry, literature, culture, and much more.

Their catalog contains some Hispanic culture favorites for children: *Amelia's Road* by Linda Jacobs Altman, the story of a young migrant worker child, $14.95; *Abuela's Weave* by Omar Castaneda, about a Guatemalan girl and her grandmother, $14.95; *The Legend of Two Moons* by Francisco Mora, based on Medican folklore, is the story of why there is only one moon in the evening sky, $15; and more.

Holiday House, Inc., 425 Madison Ave., New York NY 10017. They have a catalog of children's books.

The Day of the Dead: A Mexican-American Celebration by Diane Hoyt-Goldsmith, shows how twins Ximena and Azucena honor their deceased friends and relatives by celebrating the Day of the Dead. Ages 8-12, 32 pages, $15.95.

John Muir Publications, PO Box 613, Santa Fe NM 87504. (505) 982-4078. FAX (505) 988-1680. Toll-free 1-800-285-4078. This company has a new series of books called *Kids Explore ...* which has been drawing acclaim by experts for its content and format. These books are written for kids by kids, (the students in the Westridge Young Writers Workshop in Littleton, Colorado) and explore the diversity of American culture. Each book is 7" x 9", 112 to 144 pages, $9.95. This has been said about *Kids Explore America's Hispanic Heritage*: "An enthusiastic and genuine glimpse into the Hispanic culture that is part of our national heritage. ... This is excellent supplementary material."—*School Library Journal.*

Lectorum Publications, Inc., 137 West 14th St, New York NY 10011. (212) 929-2833. FAX (212) 727-3035. They have a catalog full of Spanish language books for children. Examples: *Hablemos del Racismo* (Let's Talk About Racism) by Angela

Grunsell, hardcover, $12.95; *Hoy es Halloween* by P.K. Hallinan, hardcover $8.95; *La Vaca Que Decía Oink* by Bernard Most, hardcover $12.95. There are many more books to choose from, such as books in the Spanish language: the Barbar series, atlases, storybooks, fiction for children, fiction for adults, reference books for children, dictionaries, novels and more.

Lee & Low Books, 228 East 45th Street, New York NY 10017. (212) 867-6155. FAX (212) 338-9059. This company produces award-winning multicultural titles for young readers. Their commitment to authenticity includes having authors working in cooperation with many outside resources to create their titles. Their titles include books about Black culture, Japanese-American culture, and Hispanic culture.

Children's titles on Hispanic culture include: the 1993 Parents' Choice Award Honoree *Abuela's Weave* by Oscar Castaneda. It is a story about a Guatemalan woman and her granddaughter who weave clothing from the heart. "A story rich in history and family tradition, to be enjoyed by many a reading."—*Smithsonian Magazine*. "A book to be read independently and enjoyed by all children."—*School Library Journal*. Ages 3-9, hardcover, $14.95. They also have *Amelia's Road* by Linda Jacobs Altman, a story about a migrant worker family, and Amelia, who discovers an "accidental road" that leads to an old tree where she finally finds a sense of permanence. "An important title for any library serving migrant populations. ... A welcome addition almost anywhere."—*School Library Journal*. "Affecting and ultimately hopeful."—*Publishers Weekly*. Ages 3-10, hardcover, $14.95.

Minnesota Historical Society Press, 345 Kellogg Blvd. West, St. Paul MN 55102-1906. (612) 296-7539. Toll-free orders 1-800-647-7827. FAX (612) 297-1345. This press has multicultural studies about Native American tribes (Sioux, Ojibway, Chippewa, Hidatsa), African American, Scandinavian, and Hispanic.

Hispanic title: *Mexican Americans in Minnesota: An Introduction to Historical Sources,* 26 pages, $3.

Museum of New Mexico Press, PO Box 2087, Santa Fe NM 87504. (505) 827-6454. FAX (505) 827-7308. This press has a lot of books about the Southwest, its Indian population, and the Hispanic influence. There are books about Pueblo Indians, Navajos, and New Mexican art and culture.

Two Hispanic books of special interest are: *Cuentos: Tales from the Hispanic Southwest* by José Griego y Maestas and Rudolfo A. Anaya. These tales evoke the rich tradition of the early Spanish settlers and their descendents. A bilingual book, 174 pages, paper, $9.95; *Rock Art in New Mexico* by Polly Schaafsma, originally published in 1972, now fully revised and expanded, is a comprehensive book on ancient and historic Native American and Hispanic rock art at sites in New Mexico, 168 pages, 190 duotone plates, paperbound, $29.95.

Piñata Books, Arte Público, University of Houston, 4800 Calhoun, Houston TX 77204-2090. (713) 743-2841. FAX (713) 743-2847. Toll-free 1-800-633-ARTE. This company has a catalog of bilingual English/Spanish books, such as *The Gift of the Poinsettia/ El Regalo de la Flo de Nochebuena* by Pat Mora and Charles Ramírez Berg. It is a picture book introducing children to the customs of Mexico, ages 3-7, $14.95 hardcover. Another colorful illustrated children's book is *Pepita Talks Twice/ Pepita habla dos veces* by Ofelia Dumas Lachtman, which tells the story of young girl who learns the value of being bilingual, ages 3-7, $14.95 hardcover.

Temple University Press, Broad and Oxford Sts., Philadelphia PA 19122. (215) 204-8787. Toll-free 1-800-447-1656. FAX (215) 204-4719. Their catalog includes scholarly books on Ethnic Studies, African American Studies, Asian American Studies, and Latino Studies.

Their Latino Studies titles include: *Going Down to the Barrio: Homeboys and Homegirls in Change* by Joan Moore, which is an illuminating sociological look at two Chicano gangs in East Los Angeles, 200 pages, paper $16.95, cloth $39.95. *New Immigrants, Old Unions: Organizing Undocumented Workers in Los Angeles* by Héctor Delgado, is a case study of a trade union led by undocumented workers at a waterbed factory in Los Angeles, 200 pages, paper $18.95, cloth $39.95.

University of Oklahoma Press, 1005 Asp Avenue, PO Box 787, Norman OK 73070-0787. Toll-free 1-800-627-7377. This University Press has a large selection of books on MesoAmerican and Latin American studies. There are books on specific prehistoric cultures, such as the Aztecs, the Toltecs, the Incas, the Zapotecs, the Mayas. There are also books about the explorers of South America.

JAPANESE CULTURE JAPANESE-AMERICANS AND JAPANESE-CANADIANS

Books Nippan, 1123 Dominguez St, Suite K, Carson CA 90746. (310) 604-9701. FAX (310) 604-1134. Order toll-free 1-800-562-1410. This company has a series of books that inform and entertain about the Japanese culture. *Japanese Family & Culture,* is a look at Japanese culture from distant past to present. Over 1000 illustrations to explain everyday family life, ceremonies, etc. Paper, $13.95. *A Look into Japan* introduces a variety of Japanese customs, traditions and lifestyles, paper, $13.95. *Japanese Characters* is a fun and easy way to learn about the complex written Japanese language, paper, $13.95. *Say It in Japanese* is a phrasebook, paper, $13.95. *Festivals of Japan* presents the festivals which highlight Japanese traditions, paper $13.95. *Tea Etiquette for Guests* has over 500 black and white photographs about the Japanese tea ceremony, softcover with jacket, $49.95. Send for catalog for full list of titles.

Chelsea House Publishers, PO Box 914, 1974 Sproul Road, Suite 400, Broomall PA 19008-0914. (610) 353-5166. Toll-free orders 1-800-362-9786. FAX (610) 359-1439. *Issei and Nissei: The Settling of Japanese America;* 128 pages, all ages, hardcover $18.95.

Children's Book Press, 6400 Hollis St., Suite 4, Emeryville CA 94608. (510) 655-3395. FAX (510) 655-1978. They publish multicultural titles for children about African-American, Hispanic, Asian-American, Jewish American, and Native American subjects. Japanese American title: *Sachiko Means Happiness* by Kimiko Sakai, is a story of a young girl's acceptance of her grandmother's Alzheimer's disease. Ages 6-12, $13.95.

Friendship Press, 475 Riverside Drive, Room 772, New York NY 10115. (212) 870-2588. This company has a complete catalog with books and other resources for global living, of which there are many for multicultural education. *Aki and the Banner of Names: And Other Stories from Japan* is about 9-year-old Aki who wants to become a messenger of peace, $4.95; teacher's guide, $5.95.

Highsmith® Inc., W5527 Highway 106, PO Box 800, Fort Atkinson, WI 53538-0800. Toll-free orders 1-800-558-2110. Toll-free customer service 1-800-558-3899. Toll-free FAX 1-800-835-2329. Highsmith is a distributor of high quality books and materials. They have a catalog called *Highsmith® Multicultural Bookstore™: Authentic Multicultural Books and Media* which has a wide selection of books for adults and children on multicultural subjects. There are children's storybooks, folktales and legends, activity books, young adult fiction and biography, literary criticism, business and finance, self help, social and political sciences, poetry, literature, culture, and much more.

Their catalog contains some popular Japanese American titles: *Baseball Saved Us* by Ken Mochizuki, about how this sport eased the pain of living in a Japanese internment camp during WWII, $14.95; *The Journey: Japanese Americans, Racism and Renewal* by Sheila Hamanaka, is about the people in the internment camps during WWII and their struggle to survive, $18.99; *Thanksgiving at Obaachan's* by Janet Mitsui Brown, is about Thanksgiving at grandmothers for a young Japanese American girl, $12.95.

KIT, Knowledge, Ideas & Trends, Inc., 1131-O Tolland Turnpike, Suite 153, Manchester CT 06040. (203) 646-0745. FAX (203) 646-3931. Their title *The Changing Worlds of Older Women in Japan* by Anne O. Freed, MSW, shows a thoughtful insight into the changing Japanese society. The author interviewed 26 elderly Japanese women, who recount their experiences and show the mechanism of coping and adjustment in Japanese society. 250 pages, cloth $27.95, paper $17.95.

Lee & Low Books, 228 East 45th Street, New York NY 10017. (212) 867-6155. FAX (212) 338-9059. This company produces award-winning multicultural titles for young readers. Their commitment to authenticity includes having authors working in cooperation with many outside resources to create their titles. Their titles include books about black culture, Japanese-American culture, and Hispanic culture.

Their children's title on Japanese-American culture is *Baseball Saved Us* by Ken Mochizuki. A young boy tells how baseball gave Japanese-Americans a sense of purpose while enduring injustice and humiliation in an internment camp. This title won a 1993 Parents' Choice Award and received the following recognition: "Best Multicultural Title."—Publishers Weekly, 1993 Cuffies Award, "Best Bets of 1993."—San Francisco Chronicle, ages 4+, hardcover, $14.95.

Shambhala, c/o Random House, Inc., 400 Hahn Road, Westminister MD 21157. Toll-free 1-800-733-3000. In Hawaii, Alaska & Maryland, call toll-free 1-800-492-0782. Publishers of the book *The Crane's Gift* by Steve Biddle, is a Japanese folktale for children about a mysterious young woman with a secret. 32 pages, hardcover, $16.

Tundra Books Inc., PO Box 1030, Plattsburgh NY 12901. (514) 932-5434. FAX (514) 484-2152. In U.S., orders should be sent to: University of Toronto Press, 340 Nagel Dr, Buffalo NY 14225. (716) 683-4547. FAX (416) 667-7832.

This Canadian-based publishing company has titles on Canada, China, Chinese Canadians, Native Americans, and Japanese-Canadians.

Their Japanese Canadian title is *A Child in Prison Camp* by Shizuye Takashima, which is about a Japanese-Canadian girl interned in WWII. " ... a poignant and beautiful little book."—*The San Francisco Chronicle.* Ages 10+, 100 pages, paper $7.95.

JEWISH CULTURE ISRAEL

Albert Whitman & Company, 6340 Oakton St., Morton Grove IL 60053-2723. (708) 581-0033. Toll-free 1-800-255-7675. FAX (708) 581-0039. *Hanukkuh* explains this holiday for ages 3-7. Paper, $4.95.

Alef Design Group, 4423 Fruitland Ave., Los Angeles CA 90058. (213) 582-1200. Toll-free 1-800-845-0662. FAX (213) 585-0327. This company produces "well-crafted Judaica." One children's book of special interest is: *A Sense of Shabbat* by Faige Kobre, with sincere photographs and simple text which help make the Jewish Sabbath come alive, 32 pages, hardcover, $11.95.

Bantam Books, 1540 Broadway, New York NY 10036. (212) 354-6500. Toll-free 1-800-223-6834. *Mrs. Katz and Tush* is the story of an old Jewish widow, a young African-American boy, and a cat named Tush. Ages 5-8, $15.

Boyds Mills Press, 815 Church St.,

Honesdale PA 18431. (717) 254-1164. FAX (717) 253-0179. Orders toll-free 1-800-949-7777. *Hanukkah, Happy Hannukkah: Crafts, recipes, games, puzzles, songs, and more for a joyous celebration of the Festival of Lights* by Jeff O'Hare. This book helps children understand the full story of Hannukkah, its meanings and its symbols. There are games, stories, and more for educational activities. Ages 5-10, paper $4.95.

Children's Book Press, 6400 Hollis St., Suite 4, Emeryville CA 94608. (510) 655-3395. FAX (510) 655-1978. Multicultural titles for children about African-American, Hispanic, Asian-American, Jewish American, and Native American subjects.

Jewish American title: *Leaving for America* by Roslyn Bresnick-Perry, showing life in a Russian Jewish community in the 1920's. "This picture book sends a strong, timeless message to children about the importance of family and honoring cultural roots."—*Small Press Magazine*. Ages 4-12, $14.95.

HarperCollins, 10 E. 53rd St., New York NY 10022. (212) 207-7000. Toll-free 1-800-331-3761. In *The Lily Cupboard* by Shulamith Oppenheim, a small Jewish girl is sent to live with a non-Jewish family during World War II. Ages 6-8, $15.

Holiday House, Inc., 425 Madison Ave., New York NY 10017. They have a catalog of children's books.

Hilde and Eli: Children of the Holocaust by David A. Adler, describes the life of Hilde and Eli, who were children during the early years of Nazi rule in Germany. They were among the one-and-a-half-million Jewish children who were victims of the Holocaust. Ages 8-12, 32 pages, $15.95.

Jewish Lights Publishing, Box 237, Sunset Farm Offices, Rt 4, Woodstock VT 05091. (802) 457-4000. FAX (802) 457-4004. *The Book of Letters: A Mystical Hebrew Alphabet* by Lawrence Kushner, tells about folktales and the exploration of the mystical meanings of the Hebrew Alphabet, hardcover $24.95.

Learning Works, PO Box 6187, Santa Barbara CA 93160. (805) 964-4220. Toll-free 1-800-235-5767. FAX (805) 964-1466. *The Jewish Question Collection* is a book of more than 300 questions on Jewish history, traditions, holidays, people, places, with answer key, for all ages, $7.95. *The Hannukkah Happening* is a children's book filled with creative games, puzzles, recipes, facts, plenty of fun, ages 7-12, $4.95.

Little Brown & Company, Time Life Building, 1271 Avenue of the Americas, New York NY 10020. (212) 522-8700. Toll-free 1-800-343-9204. *Songs of Chanukah* compiled by Jeanne Modesitt, has traditional and contemporary songs, $15.95.

Longstreet Press, 2140 Newmarket Parkway, Suite 118, Marietta GA 30067. (404) 980-1488. Toll-free 1-800-927-1488. FAX (404) 859-9894. *The Yiddish are Coming* by Robyn Cohen and Robyn Rousso, is a pictorial primer of one of the world's most colorful languages. This book offers dozens of words and phrases, such as chootzpah, kibbutz, zhlob, and shlock. The Yiddish words are incorporated into rhyming stanzas with English translations and a pronunciation guide. Paperback, $8.95.

Temple University Press, Broad and Oxford Sts., Philadelphia PA 19122. (215) 204-8787. Toll-free 1-800-447-1656. FAX (215) 204-4719. Their catalog includes scholarly books on Ethnic Studies, African American Studies, Asian American Studies, and Latino Studies.

Their Ethnic Studies Section includes these Jewish titles: *Jewish Identity,* which contains essays that discuss the nature of Jewishness and the significance of cultural identity, 344 pages, paper, $19.95, cloth $49.95. Also available is *Consider and Hear Me: Voices from Palestine and Israel* by Saul Slapikoff. The author's accounts of his trips to Israel and the Occupied Territories describes rarely-heard perspectives, 240 pages, paper $16.95, cloth $34.95.

Viking Penguin, 375 Hudson St., New York NY 10014. (212) 366-2000. Toll-free 1-800-331-4624. *In the Month of Kislev* by Jina Jaffe is a story of Mendel, who is so poor that the only way to get his children latkes is to take them to the front of the store of the rich man, Fievel, and to smell them. Fievel becomes angry and tells the rabbi that the family should pay for smelling the latkes. Ages 4-8, $15.

NATIVE AMERICAN

Alaska Native Language Center, University of Alaska Fairbanks, PO Box 757680, Fairbanks AK 99775-7680. (907) 474-7874. FAX (907) 474-6586. This organization was established in 1972 by state legislation as a center for research and documentation of the state's 20 native languages. They have an extensive list of publications.

Of particular interest: *As My Grandfather Told It: Traditional Stories from the Koyukuk* as told by Catherine Attla, in native language and in English, in rhythmic prose, $18; *The Legacy of a Taku River Tlingit Clan* by Elizabeth Nyman and Jeff Leer, a bilingual book, has six narrative texts relating to ancient legends and traditional stories, $26.95.

Baker House Books, PO Box 6287, Grand Rapids MI 49516-6287. (616) 676-9185. Toll-free wholesale orders only 1-800-877-2665. Toll-free FAX for wholesale orders only 1-800-398-3111. FAX (616) 676-9573. This company has books about Indian children and their adventures by author Ken Thomasma. (Editor's note: My daughter loved these books as a child, especially *Naya Nuki*). The titles are: *Naya Nuki: Shoshoni Girl Who Ran,* is about a girl who traveled alone in the wilderness for more than a month and eventually returned to her people, showing courage and survival skills. *Soun Tetoken: Nez Perce Boy Tames a Stallion,* is about an 1877 speechless orphan befriending a stallion and undergoing his initiation into manhood. *Om-kas-koe: Blackfeet Twin Captures an Elkdog*, is about twins who discover a strange animal never seen before by the tribe. *Kunu: Winnebago Boy Escapes* is about a boy and his grandfather who attempt a daring river escape after a forced march to a South Dakota reservation. *Pathki Nana: Kooenai Girl Solves a Mystery* about a shy girl who must go into the mountains to seek a guardian spirit, and the result is a life-and-death struggle. This book won a Wyoming Children's Book Award. Each book: cloth $10.99, paper $6.99.

Chelsea House Publishers, PO Box 914, 1974 Sproul Road, Suite 400, Broomall PA 19008-0914. (610) 353-5166. Toll-free orders 1-800-362-9786. FAX (610) 359-1439. Send for the catalog called *Chelsea House Presents the Best in Indian Studies* which features Indians of North America, the Junior Library of American Indians, North American Indians of Achievement, a video collection, and more.

Their *Indians of North America Series* provides cultural information about various tribes. Each title offers a comprehensive profile of a particular tribe with photographs, paintings, maps, and a feature on

Indian art and artifacts. There are 66 hardcover titles, and 23 paperback titles, including: *The Hopi; The Nez Perce; The Pueblo; The Cherokee; The Crow; The Seminole; The Navajos; the Yankton Sioux; Women in American Indian Society;* etc. Each book is 96 to 144 pages, ages 10+, hardcover $18.95, paper $7.95.

For young readers, there's the *Junior Library of American Indians*. There are over 30 titles: *The Hopi Indians; The Maya Indians; The Pueblo Indians; The Seminole Indians; The Teton Sioux Indians; The Cheyenne Indians; The Navajo Indians;* etc. Each book is 72 to 80 pages, ages 8-12, hardcover $18.95, paper $6.95.

Another series is the *North American Indians of Achievement*. There are more than 20 titles: *Geronimo; Black Hawk; Crazy Horse; Sitting Bull; Pocahontas; Jim Thorpe; Chochise; Ben Nighthorse Campbell; Will Rogers*; etc. Each book is 104 to 128 pages, ages 10+, hardcover $18.95, paper $7.95.

The Sioux is a lively look at this past culture with detailed illustrations, photographs. It examines the clothing, food, family life, and religion of the people. Includes a traditional story and activities that can be performed at home. Ages 8-12, grade 3-7, paper $6.95.

Children's Book Press, 6400 Hollis St., Suite 4, Emeryville CA 94608. (510) 655-3395. FAX (510) 655-1978. They have multicultural titles for children about African-American, Hispanic, Asian-American, Jewish American, and Native American subjects.

Books about Acoma culture are:*The People Shall Continue* by Simon Ortiz. "The best overview of Native history for younger children that I have ever seen."—*Books Without Bias*. Ages 7-12, $14.95. Books about Chickasaw culture: *Baby Rattlesnake* by Te Ata and Lynn Moroney. "Outstanding Native American story of family love and forgiveness."—*Bookwatch.* Ages 4-12, $13.95.

Children's Press®, 5440 North Cumberland Ave., Chicago IL 60656-1494. Toll-free 1-800-621-1115. FAX 1-800-374-4329. This publisher has an extensive line of fine books for kids, and there are many good multicultural titles.

They have a large number of books on Native American tribes: *Anasazi, Cherokee, Cheyenne, Crow, Hopi, Navajo, Nez Perce, Pawnee, Seminole, Sioux,* and more, each

$4.95. There are biographies: *Chief Joseph of the Nez Perce Indians: Champion of Liberty, Sacagawea: Indian Interpreter to Lewis and Clark, Susette La Flesche: Advocate for Native American Rights, Charles Eastman: Physician, Reformer, and Native American Leader,* each $5.95.

Consortium Book Sales and Distribution, 1045 Westgate Drive, St. Paul MN 55114-1065. Toll-free orders 1-800-283-3572. FAX (612) 221-0124. This book distributor has a children's catalog full of multicultural titles.

An Anasazi Welcome by Kay Matthews shows an Anasazi ghost who teaches a family how to respect the land and also the different kinds of people and animals who dwell on it. Ages 4-8, paper, $6.95.

Chocolate, Chipmunks, and Canoes: An American Indian Words Coloring Book by Juan Alvarez. This book helps children learn new words from Navajo, Hopi, Pueblo, Cree, Dakota, Inuit, and other Native American languages. Ages 2-5, $3.95.

Mystery at Echo Cliffs by Kate Abbott is a mystery set in the Four Corners region. Ages 10-14, paper $11.95.

The Navajo Brothers and the Stolen Herd by Maurine Grammer is the story of two Navajo teens who regain their family's sheep from thieves. Ages 10-14, paper $9.95.

Council Oak Books, 1350 East 15th St., Tulsa OK 74120. (918) 587-6454. FAX (918) 583-4995. *White Bead Ceremony* by Sherrin Watkins, is about how Mary Greyfeather's grandmother suggests a Shawnee naming ceremony, hardcover, $16.95. *Cherokee Animal Tales* are simple stories of animal pranks, which are told with humor and charm, $7.95.

Dial, 375 Hudson St., New York NY 10014. (212) 366-2000. *Brother Eagle, Sister Sky* is a moving book that shows Native American concern for the environment long before it was politically correct and socially popular. It has beautiful paintings. Ages 6+, $16.

Essential Learning Products, 2300 West Fifth Avenue, PO Box 2590, Columbus OH 43216-2590. (614) 486-0633. FAX (614) 487-2272. *Anna's Athabascan Summer* tells about how Anna learns about the beautiful ways of her native culture, ages 4-8, hardcover, $14.95.

Four Winds Trading Company, 685 South Broadway, Suite A, Boulder CO 80303. (303) 499-4484. Toll-free 1-800-456-5444. FAX (303) 499-6640. This company specializes in Native American music, literature, and products.

Their catalog contains numerous wonderful books about Native Americans, with topics such as biographies, arts & crafts, cookery, cultural legacy, history, and literature.

Biographies include: the famous *Black Elk Speaks: Being the Life Story of a Holy Man of the Oglala Sioux*, $12.95, (also available as an audio book); *Crazy Horse: The Strange Man of the Oglalas* by Mari Sandoz, which is in its 50th anniversary edition, $11.95; *Geronimo: The Man, His Time, His Place* by Angie Debo, which not only is a definitive book on Geronimo, but also very illustrative of the Apache wars, $17.95; *Brave Are My People,* edited by Frank Waters, is a collection of 20 profiles of North America's greatest Indian leaders, $24.95.

Arts and crafts books include books on beadwork, kachina dolls, and baskets.

Cultural legacy and history books on Native Americans found in this catalog are: *The People Called Apache* by Thomas E. Mails, which is devoted to the renowned Arizona and New Mexico Apache. It has detailed information on their culture with lavish illustrations and previously unpublished photographs, 608 pages, $49.98; *Native American Dance: Ceremonies and Social Traditions* edited by Charlotte Heth, has over 200 mostly color photos which celebrate survival and adaptation, hardcover, $45, paper $29.95; *Trail of Tears: The Rise and Fall of the Cherokee Nation* by John Ehle, is about the horrendous forced exile of the Cherokee which is known as the "trail of tears," 432 pages, $11; and of course the famous *Bury My Heart at Wounded Knee* by Dee Brown, in its 20th anniversary edition of the book. It has sold over 4 million copies in 17 languages, 487 pages, paper, $14.95.

The literature they have available includes the treasure *The Education of Little Tree* by Forrest Carter, which is one of this editor's personal favorites, 216 pages, $10.95. Also available: *Ceremony* by Leslie Marmon Silko, is about a young American Indian who was imprisoned by WW2 Japanese and horrified by his captivity, 261 pages, paper, $9; *Mean Spirit* by Linda Hogan, about the 1920's Osage people living in Oklahoma when oil was discovered, 388 pages, $4.99.

There's a special section on children's and educational books: *Keepers of the Night: Native Ameri-*

can Stories and Nocturnal Activities for Children by Joseph Bruchac & Michael Caduto. It has field-tested, hands-on activities for teaching children how to connect with the natural world by looking at it at night, 146 pages, $14.95; *Keepers of the Animals: Native American Stories & Wildlife Activities for Children* by Joseph Bruchac & Michael Caduto, is again, a wonderful book for teaching kids, cloth, $22.95, teachers' guide, $9.95; *Native American Stories* told by Joseph Bruchac, this collection of 24 stories from many Native American cultures, paper, $11.95, also available on two-tape audio set. *Two Legged Creature: An Otoe Story* by Anna Lee Walters, is a story about how man came to live with the animals and how animals showed him how to live. Soon this two-legged creature began to live destructively. This story draws on Native American values to teach us how we are to live in the world. Hardcover, $14.95.

Franklin Watts, 95 Madison Ave., New York NY 10016. (212) 686-7070. Toll-free 1-800-621-1115. FAX 1-800-374-4329. This company has a series of *First Books* that feature illustrations, photographs, and information appropriate for children. Within this series, there are several titles on Native Americans: *The Chilula; The Comanches; The Hopi; The Nez Perce; The Pomo*. Each $5.95 paper.

Friendship Press, 475 Riverside Drive, Room 772, New York NY 10115. (212) 870-2588. This company has a complete catalog with books and other resources for global living, of which there are many for multicultural education.

Crickets and Corn: Five Stories About Native North American Children by Peg Black, is about children from five different tribes who make important discoveries about what it means to be Native people, $3.50.

Greenfield Review Press, PO Box 308, 2 Middle Grove Road, Greenfield Center NY 12833. (518) 583-1440. FAX (518) 583-9741. They have an entire catalog called "North American Native Authors Catalog." This 50-page catalog contains titles on legends, history, biographies, Native women, sacred traditions, dance and ceremony, crafts and skills, education and resources, fiction, poetry, and music.

Their books on legends include: *Wigwam Evenings* by Charles Eastman (Sioux), a collection of Sioux legends, $8; *American Indian Myths and Legends* edited by Richard Erdoes and Alfonso Ortiz, this book contains 160 tales from 80 tribes, $17.

Histories include: *The Wampanoags of Mashpee* by Russell Peters, is about a tribe who inhabit Massachusetts, Cape Cod and the islands, $16; *Meet the Lakota, Volume One: The People* by LaVera Rose, written in English and Lakota, $5.95.

Biographies include: *Growing Up Native American* edited by Patricia Riley, along with 22 Native American writers tell about their childhood, $9.95; *Rooted Like the Ash Trees* is a collection of writings by members of New England tribes, $5.

Resources for education include: *Through Indian Eyes: The Native Experience in Books for Children* by Doris Seale and Beverly Slapin, is a guide to children's books by and about Native Americans, written for educators, parents & librarians, $24.95; *Resource Reading List* is a bibliography of books by and about Native Americans, $15.

Reading books for children include titles from Jeanette Armstrong (Okanagan): *Neekna and Chemai*, is the story of two little girls growing up with Okanagan life before the coming of the white man, $12.95; *How Food Was Given*, $12.95; *How Turtle Set the Animals Free*, traditional Okanagan legends, $4.95; and more.

Heyday Books, PO Box 9145, Berkeley CA 94709. (510) 549-3564. FAX (510) 549-1889. This company has several titles on California Indians. One popular title is *The Way We Lived: California Indian Stories, Songs, and Reminiscences* edited by Malcolm Margolin, with love songs, death chants, legends, and oral histories about native culture in California, 260 pages, paper $14.95. A children's version of this book is *Native Ways: California Indian Stories and Memories* for fourth and fifth grade reading levels, 128 pages, $7.95.

Ararapíkva: Traditional Karuk Indian Literature from Northwestern California, a translation by Julian Lang, is a bilingual book in Karuk and English, with sacred tales and more. "More than a tantalizing collection of myths"—*Publishers Weekly*, 122 pages, paper $10.95. *The Maidu Indian Myths and Stories of Hac'ibyjim* is a translation by William Shipley and includes such myths as how the earth was made, of the sisters who married the stars, and more. "Gone to great lengths to maintain the oral, theatrical quality ... Sensitively handled, the narratives take on a Homeric timbre." —*Publishers Weekly,* 192 pages, paper $12.95.

Highsmith® Inc., W5527 Highway 106, PO Box 800, Fort Atkinson, WI 53538-0800. Toll-free orders 1-800-558-2110. Toll-free customer service 1-800-558-3899. Toll-free FAX 1-800-835-2329. Highsmith is a distributor of high quality books and materials. They have a catalog called *Highsmith® Multicultural Bookstore™: Authentic Multicultural Books and Media* which has a wide selection of books for adults and children on multicultural subjects. There are children's storybooks, folktales and legends, activity books, young adult fiction and biography, literary criticism, business and finance, self help, social and political sciences, poetry, literature, culture, and much more.

Some of the popular Native American titles are found in their catalog are: *Julie of the Wolves* by Jean Craighead George, a tale of a young Eskimo girl who is lost and cared for by the wolves, $3.95; *The Woman Who Fell From the Sky: The Iroquois Story of Creation* by John Bierhorst, $15; *Two Little Girls Lost in the Bush: A Cree Story for Children* by Glecia Bear, $14.95. There's also the Alvin Josephy's Biography Series of American Indians. Send for a catalog to see the full list of books.

Holiday House, Inc., 425 Madison Ave., New York NY 10017. They have a catalog of children's books.

The Nez Perce: A First Americans Book by popular author Virginia Driving Hawk Sneve, retells the creation myth of the Nez Perce Indians and then relates their history, customs, and facts about the tribe today. Ages 7-11, 32 pages, $15.95. There are other First Americans Books about the Seminoles, the Sioux, and the Navajos.

John Muir Publications, PO Box 613, Santa Fe NM 87504. (505) 982-4078. FAX (505) 988-1680. Toll-free 1-800-285-4078. This company has a new series of books called *Kids Explore ...* which has been drawing acclaim by experts for its content and format. These books are written for kids by kids, (the students in the Westridge Young Writers Workshop in Littleton, Colorado) and explore the diversity of American culture. Each book is 7" x 9", 112 to 144 pages, $9.95. *Kids Explore the Heri-*

tage of Western Native Americans was written by the kids as they ventured into the western states to meet six Native American families. Each chapter features biographies of the family members and their accomplishments, as well as some of their favorite stories, crafts and recipes.

Minnesota Historical Society Press, 345 Kellogg Blvd. West, St. Paul MN 55102-1906. (612) 296-7539. Toll-free orders 1-800-647-7827. FAX (612) 297-1345. This press has multicultural studies about Native American tribes (Sioux, Ojibway, Chippewa, Hidatsa), African American, Scandinavian, and Hispanic.

The Ojibwa of Western Canada, 1780 to 1870, by Laura Peers, explores the questions of cultural change and adaptation. The result is a clearly written history that reveals both the changes the Ojibwa chose to make and the continuity within the culture they retained. 320 pages, cloth $32.95, paper $15.95. *Dictionary of the Ojibway Language,* by Frederic Baraga, 736 pages, $24.95. *History of the Ojibway People* by William Warren, includes not only history but descriptions of their customs, family life, totemic system, hunting methods, and relations with other cultures. 411 pages, $12.95.

Sioux books include: *Little Crow: Spokesman for the Sioux* by Gary Clayton Anderson, 259 pages, $10.95; *Through Dakota Eyes: Narrative Accounts of the Minnesota Indian War of 1862* by Gary Clayton Anderson, which is a collection of 36 narratives that present the Dakota Indians' point-of-view about this conflict, 316 pages, $11.95; *Dakota-English Dictionary,* 680 pages, $24.95.

Hidatsa books include: *Buffalo Bird Woman's Garden: Agriculture of the Hidatsa Indians,* describes her gardening methods and traditional recipes, 129 pages, $8.95; *Goodbird the Indian: His Story* by Edward Goodbird, is a memoir first published in 1914. It shows Hidatsa people's life on the early reservation, 78 pages, $5.95.

Museum of New Mexico Press, PO Box 2087, Santa Fe NM 87504. (505) 827-6454. FAX (505) 827-7308. This press has a lot of books about the Southwest, its Indian population, and the Hispanic influence. There are books about Pueblo Indians, Navajos, and New Mexican art and culture.

Two Native American books of special interest are: *I Am Here: Two Thousand Years of Southwest*

Indian Arts and Culture, showing material culture from some of the finest collections of Southwest Indian art and artifacts of the nation, 256 pages, 90 color plates, 150 black and white photos, paperbound $39.95; *Rock Art in New Mexico* by Polly Schaafsma, originally published in 1972, now fully revised and expanded, is a comprehensive book on ancient and historic Native American and Hispanic rock art at sites in New Mexico, 168 pages, 190 duotone plates, paperbound, $29.95.

National Archives, Trust Fund Boards, Washington DC 20408. Toll-free 1-800-788-6282. FAX (301) 763-6025. *Guide to Records in the National Archives Relating to American Indians* was compiled by Edward Hill. This guide the enables the reader to review descriptions of records that are available in the National Archives and in its regional archives that concern federal Indian policy, the effects of national policies on Indian culture, Indian wars and their results, and the role of Native Americans in the development of U.S. society, 467 pages, hardcover $25.

Native Experience, The, 7406 Waldron Ave., Temple Hills MD 20748. (319) 449-6730. Toll-free 1-800-652-6730. This group publishes *The Native American Experience Newsletter* which reviews and distributes books written by Native American authors or about Native American subjects. They have over 1,000 active titles and 10,000 backlist titles.

Naturegraph Publishers, Inc., Box 1075, 3543 Indian Creek Road, Happy Camp CA 96039. (916) 493-5353. Toll-free 1-800-390-5353. FAX (916) 493-5240. This publisher specializes in books about nature and Native Americans.

They have many good reading books about Native American topics, such as: *Shasta Indian Tales*, with tales of the Shasta Indian tribe of Northern California, including the creation story, stories of the animals, and more, $5.95; *Apache Legends* by Lou Cuevas, are stories by Lou Cuevas' grandfather about the origin of many desert or prairie creatures, such as the rattlesnake and the buffalo, $8.95; *Osage: Life and Legends* by Robert Liebert, combines many aspects of Osage life, their livelihood, social organization and spirituality, $8.95; *Broken Pattern: Sunlight and Shadows of Hopi History* by Vada Carlson, shows the traumatic coming of the Spanish into the American Southwest, $8.95.

Northland Publishing, PO Box 1389, 2900 N. Fort Valley Road, Flagstaff, AZ 86001. (602) 774-5251. Toll-free 1-800-346-3257. FAX (602) 774-0592. This company has a specialty of Native American titles, especially about Indians of the Southwest.

Some of the titles include: *Dictionary of Prehistoric Indian Artifacts of the American Southwest* by Franklin Barrett, $12.95; *Hopi Kachinas: The Complete Guide to Collecting Kachina Dolls* by Barton Wright, is their bestselling title with over 125,000 sold, $12.95; *Ancient Ruins of the Southwest* by David Noble, $14.95.

Tundra Books Inc., PO Box 1030, Plattsburgh NY 12901. (514) 932-5434. FAX (514) 484-2152. In U.S., orders should be sent to: University of Toronto Press, 340 Nagel Dr, Buffalo NY 14225. (716) 683-4547. FAX (416) 667-7832.

This Canadian-based publishing company has titles on Canada, China, Chinese Canadians, Native Americans, and Japanese-Canadians.

Their Native American titles include: *How We Saw the World* by C.J. Taylor, which are native stories of the origin of people. These legends come from Chuckchee, Cree, Mandan, Modoc, Mohawk, Osage and Zuni peoples. Ages 8+, 32 pages, hardcover, $17.95.

The following titles are all for ages 8+, by C.J. Taylor, are 24 pages each, hardcover $13.95: *The Secret of the White Buffalo: An Oglala Sioux Legend; How Two-Feather Was Saved From Loneliness: An Abenaki Legend; The Ghost and Lone Warrior: An Arapaho Legend; Little Water and the Gift of the Animals: A Seneca Legend.*

They have a *Native American Dwellings Series.* Each book is for ages 8-12, by Bonnie Shemie, which covers the dwellings of a specific culture, hardcover $13.95. "A magic combination of text and image."—*The Hungry Mind Review.* "Highly useful."—*Booklist.* Titles in this series are: *Mounds of Earth and Shell: The Southeast; Houses of Hide and Earth: The Plains; Houses of Bark: Woodlands; Houses of Snow, Skin and Bones: The Far North; Houses of Wood: Northwest Coast.*

University of Oklahoma Press, 1005 Asp Avenue, PO Box 787, Norman OK 73070-0787. Toll-free 1-800-627-7377. This University Press has long been known for their large selection of titles on Native American topics. They have a catalog of almost 300 books about the Indians of North, Central & South America. There are numerous books on specific tribes (such as Sioux, Apache, Kiowa, Mohave, Navajo, Nez Perce, Cherokee, Pawnee, Comanche, just to name a few) and Native American historical and contemporary issues. Besides those, there are a couple interesting educational titles that might also be of special interest to parents and teachers: *The Indian Tipi: Its History, Construction and Use,* 366 pages, $16.95; *Indian Dances of North America,* 538 pages, $22.95.

GENERAL MULTICULTURAL

Albert Whitman & Company, 6340 Oakton St., Morton Grove IL 60053-2723. (708) 581-0033. Toll-free 1-800-255-7675. FAX (708) 581-0039. *Black, White, Just Right!* by Irene Trivas, is about the daughter of an interracial marriage. "This book shows how families are composed of distinct individuals whose love is the key to securing a child's sense of self."—*Publishers Weekly.* Grades 1-3, 32 pgs, $13.95.

August House, PO Box 3223, Little Rock AR 72203. (501) 372-5450. Toll-free 1-800-284-8784. FAX (501) 372-5579. This company has two excellent multicultural storytelling books for children. One is

Thirty-Three Multicultural Tales to Tell by Pleasant DeSpain, with stories from Brazil, China, Korea, Russia, Tibet, Africa, America, and more. These stories celebrate the interconnectedness of people, animals, and cultures in order to show the strength of boys, girls, men and women. 128 pages, hardback $25, paper $15. The other is *Ready-to-Tell Tales,* edited by David Holt and Bill Mooney, which has tales from Greece, Egypt, Japan, the British Isles, Mexico, Thailand, African-American, Cajun, Appalachian, Jewish, and Native American oral traditions. 224 pages, hardcover $24.95, paper $16.95.

Children's Book Store Distribution, 67 Wall St., Suite 2411, New York NY 10005. Toll-free 1-800-668-0242. *Can You Hear My Voice,* is a 50-minute, participatory show for students in grades 1-6. Through humor, storytelling, rap, songs and theatre, Kim and Jerry Broey explore what it's like to be in another person's shoes. Their music focuses on the issues of diversity and conflict resolution.

Consortium Book Sales and Distribution, 1045 Westgate Drive, St. Paul MN 55114-1065. Toll-free orders 1-800-283-3572. FAX (612) 221-0124. This book distributor has a children's catalog full of multicultural titles.

Who Belongs Here? An American Story by Margy Burns Knights won an award for Best Multicultural Title, 1993 Publishers Weekly Of-the-Cuff Awards. Based on the story of Nary, a young Cambodian immigrant, this picture book asks pertinent questions about racism and political activism. Showing Nary's experiences with name-calling and harassment, the author makes children think about who really 'belongs' in this country. Ages 5+, hardcover, $16.95.

Talking Walls by Margy Burns Knight has also drawn considerable attention. This was one of *Boston Globe's* Top Ten Non-Fiction Children's Books 1992, Finalist in *Hungry Mind Review* Children's Book of Distinction, 1993, and more. The author relates stories of walls throughout time and around the world, and in doing so, "has found a powerful theme for introducing children to the world and its diverse cultures: walls."—*Booklist.* Ages 5+, hardcover, $17.95; paper $9.95.

Tatterhood and Other Tales edited by Ethel Johnston Phelps is a collection of 25 traditional tales from around the world, all with heroines of spirit, courage and wit. Ages 6+, paper

$9.95.

Writing Across Cultures: A Handbook on Writing Poetry & Lyrical Prose by Edna Kovac is an innovative approach—using a wide range of cultural approaches to encourage lyrical writing. Paper, $11.95.

Dutton, 375 Hudson St., New York NY 10014. (212) 366-2000. *Magical Tales From Many Lands* by Margaret Mayo is a collection of stories from India, Africa, Peru, Australia, China, Japan and other lands. Ages 8+, $19.95.

Essential Learning Products, 2300 West Fifth Avenue, PO Box 2590, Columbus OH 43216-2590. (614) 486-0633. FAX (614) 487-2272. *Sleep Rhymes Around the World* is a collection of lullabies from 17 counties. The images give children a better understanding of people in other lands, age 4-10, hardcover $16.95. *Street Rhymes Around the World* is a collection of chants, songs, counting games and more from 17 countries, ages 4-10, hardcover, $16.95.

Free Spirit Publishing Inc., 400 First Avenue North, Suite 616, Minneapolis MN 55401-1730. (612) 338-2068. Orders toll-free 1-800-735-7323. FAX (612) 337-5050. Their title *Respecting Our Differences* by Lynn Duvall helps teens learn more about the people around them. It asks and answers such questions as: What is prejudice and where does it come from? Is it OK to tell sexist, racist or ethnic jokes even if I'm just kidding? These true stories show young people who have made the commitment to become more tolerant. Ages 12+, 208 pages, paper $12.95.

Friendship Press, 475 Riverside Drive, Room 772, New York NY 10115. (212) 870-2588. *A World of Children's Stories* edited by Anne Pellowski, 192 pages, hardcover, $19.95. This book contains stories from around the world organized by continent.

Highsmith® Inc., W5527 Highway 106, PO Box 800, Fort Atkinson, WI 53538-0800. Toll-free orders 1-800-558-2110. Toll-free customer service 1-800-558-3899. Toll-free FAX 1-800-835-2329. Highsmith is a distributor of high quality books and materials. They have a catalog called *Highsmith® Multicultural Bookstore™: Authentic Multicultural Books and Media* which has a wide selection of books for adults and children on multicultural subjects. There are children's storybooks, folktales and legends, activity books, young adult fiction and biography, literary criticism, business and finance, self help, social and political sciences, poetry, literature, culture, and much more.

Two popular children's books about multicultural families found in this catalog are: *Black is Brown is Tan* by Arnold Adoff, which is an award-winning story focusing on a multicultural family and the importance of maintaining a sense of identity and worth, hardcover $14.95, paper $3.95; *Black, White, Just Right!* by Marguerite Davol, is about when cultures and colors combine, to show the best of both worlds, $13.95.

Hillcrest Press, Inc., 3412 W. MacArthur Blvd, Unit G, Santa Ana CA 92704. *Ethnic L.A.* by Zena Pearlstone is a study of Los Angeles, the melting pot for people from more than 140 countries. Los Angeles is the second largest Mexican, Armenian, Korean, Filipino, Salvadoran and Guatemalan city in the world. $12.95.

Learning Works, PO Box 6187, Santa Barbara CA 93160. (805) 964-4220. Toll-free 1-800-235-5767. FAX (805) 964-1466. *Celebrate! Holidays Around the World!* This book provides information, activities and a coloring page on 14 holidays such as Chinese New Year, Tet, Kwanzaa, Green Corn Dance, and more. Ages 5-9, $4.95. *Holiday Art a la Carte* is a bonanza of 77 easy, illustrated ideas for holiday art projects, such as American Indian Day, United Nations Day, etc, ages 9-13, $9.95.

Northland Publishing, PO Box 1389, 2900 N. Fort Valley Road, Flagstaff, AZ 86001. (602) 774-5251. Toll-free 1-800-346-3257. FAX (602) 774-0592. *Less Than Half, More Than Whole* by Kathleen and Michael Lacapa, is a book for all children of multicultural backgrounds who struggle with the question, "Where do I belong?" Ages 5+, 40 pages, hardcover, $14.95.

Penguin USA, 375 Hudson St., New York NY 10014. (212) 366-2272. *Unsettling America: An Anthology of Contemporary Multicultural Poetry* by Maria Mazziotti Gillan & Jennifer Gillan, is an anthology comprised of poems that stretches across the boundaries of skin color, language, ethnicity and religion. Paper $13.95.

Robert Rinehart Publishers, PO Box 666, Niwot CO 80544. Toll-free 1-800-352-1985. *Tales of Virtues and*

Wisdoms by Toni Knapp, is a collection of legends and folktales from around the world adapted to accompany 15 original paintings of animals. Cloth, $15.95.

Stemmer House Publishers, Inc. 2627 Caves Road, Owings Mills MD 21117. (410) 363-3690. This company has a series called the *International Design Library*. These books are composed of designs from various cultures, such as Nigerian, Aztec, Northwest Indian, Plains Indians, Peruvian textiles, Scandinavian, Chinese cut-outs, Egyptian, Japanese, etc. There's a long list of these books, each $5.95.

Tilbury House, Publishers, The Boston Building, 132 Water St, Gardiner ME 04345. Trade accounts toll-free ordering 1-800-283-3572, Individual orders toll-free 1-800-582-1899. Distributed by: Consortium Book Sales and Distribution, listed in this book.

Who Belongs Here? An American Story by Margy Burns Knights won an award for Best Multicultural Title, 1993 Publishers Weekly Of-the-Cuff Awards. It is based on the story of Nary, a young Cambodian immigrant, this picture book asks pertinent questions about racism and political activism. Showing Nary's experiences with name-calling and harassment, the author makes children think about who really 'belongs' in this country. Ages 5+, hardcover, $16.95.

Talking Walls by Margy Burns Knight has also drawn considerable attention. This was one of *Boston Globe's* Top Ten Non-Fiction Children's Books in 1992 and a Finalist in *Hungry Mind Review* Children's Book of Distinction in 1993. The author relates stories of walls throughout time and around the world, and in doing so, "has found a powerful theme for introducing children to the world and its diverse cultures: walls."—*Booklist.* Ages 5+, hardcover, $17.95; paper $9.95.

University of Illinois Press, 1325 South Oak St., Champaign IL 61820. Toll-free 1-800-545-4703. This press has an extensive Ethnic Studies list which specializes in books on ethnic groups within specific regions or cities of the United States. It includes groups such as: Norwegians in Chicago, Italians in Buffalo, a Mennonite community, Germans in Chicago, Japanese in Oregon's Hood River Valley, Italian-Americans in St. Louis, Irish in Chicago, Mexican citrus worker village in Southern California, etc.

University Press of New England, 23 South Main St, Hanover NJ 03755-2048. FAX (603) 643-1550. Order toll-free 1-800-421-1561. Their title *American Identities: Contemporary Multicultural Voices* edited by Robert Pack and Jay Parini, explains that the American experience is not a single experience, but a multiplicity of experiences. These poems, stories and essays describe in moving terms what it means to be black and American, or Latino and American, or Jewish and American within this society. 416 pages, cloth, $29.95.

Another one of their titles explores how the world is now being defined in global as well as regional and national terms. *Global Cultures: A Transnational Short Fiction Reader* edited by Elisabeth Young-Bruehl contains stories from India, Cuba, South Africa, Nigeria, Uruguay, etc. These are woven together in a way to highlight how these worldwide cultures converge and diverge. 480 pages, cloth $45, paper, $19.95.

HOT PICKS

This section is the editor's choice of the best reading books for multicultural education.

ASIA, ASIAN AMERICAN

Who Belongs Here? An American Story by Margy Burns Knights, Consortium Book Sales and Distribution.

A Little Tiger in the Chinese Night by Song Nan Zhang. Tundra Books, Inc.

The Girl Who Wanted to Hunt: A Siberian Tale, Holiday House, Inc.

The Forbidden Stitch: An Asian American Women's Anthology, Calyx.

BLACK CULTURE, AFRICA & AFRICAN AMERICANS

African Ark: People and Ancient Cultures of Ethiopia and the Horn of Africa, Abrams.

Things I Like About Grandma by Francine Haskins. Children's Book Press.

Journey Toward Freedom: The Story of Sojourner Truth by Jacqueline Bernard. Consortium Book Sales and Distribution.

Born of the Sun: A Namibian Novel by Joseph Diescho. Friendship Press.

Kids Explore America's African American Heritage: John Muir Publications.

The Dreamkeepers: Successful Teachers of African American Children by Gloria Ladson-Billings. Jossey-Bass Inc., Publishers.

Afro-Bets® I'm Gonna Be by Wade Hudson. Just Us Books.

Afro-Bets® Book of Black Heroes from A to Z by Wade Hudson and Valerie Wilson Wesley. Just Us Books.

Afro-Bets® First Book About Africa by Veronica Freeman Ellis. Just Us

Books.

Joshua's Masaii Mask by Dakari Hru. Lee & Low Books.

Bein' With You This Way by W. Nikola-Lisa. Lee & Low Books.

The Singing Man, Holiday House, Inc.

Mufaro's Beautiful Daughters, Lothrop, Lee & Shephard.

From Cakewalks to Concert Halls: An Illustrated History of African American Popular Music from 1895 to 1930, Inland Book Company.

Neate to the Rescue by Debbi Chocolate. Just Us Books.

EUROPEAN CULTURE

Norwegian Proverbs, Penfield Press.

HAWAIIAN CULTURE

Maui Mouse's Supper, Bess Press.

Learn Hawaii at Home, Bess Press.

Talking Story with Nona Beamer, Bess Press.

Hawaii: Our Island State, Bess Press.

HISPANIC CULTURE, SOUTH AMERICA CENTRAL AMERICA

Family Pictures by Carmen Lomas Garza. Children's Book Press.

Atariba and Niguayona by Harriet Rohmer and Jesus Guerrero Rea. Children's Book Press.

Kids Explore America's Hispanic Heritage: John Muir Publications.

Abuela's Weave by Oscar Castaneda. Lee & Low Books.

Amelia's Road by Linda Jacobs Altman. Lee & Low Books.

The Day of the Dead: A Mexican-American Celebration, Holiday House, Inc.

Family Pictures by Carmen Lomas Garza. Children's Book Press.

JAPAN, JAPANESE-AMERICANS

Baseball Saved Us by Ken Mochizuki. Lee & Low Books.

A Child in Prison Camp, by Shizuye Takashima. Tundra Books.

JEWISH CULTURE, ISRAEL

The Jewish Question Collection, Learning Works.

A Sense of Shabbat. Alef Design Group.

Hilde and Eli: Children of the Holocaust , Holiday House, Inc.

Leaving for America by Roslyn Bresnick-Perry. Children's Book Press.

NATIVE AMERICAN

Naya Nuki: Shoshoni Girl Who Ran, by Ken Thomasma. Baker House Books.

Indians of North America Series, Chelsea House Publishers.

Baby Rattlesnake by Te Ata and Lynn Moroney. Children's Book Press.

Black Elk Speaks: Being the Life Story of a Holy Man of the Oglala Sioux, Four Winds Trading Company.

Geronimo: The Man, His Time, His Place by Angie Debo. Four Winds Trading Company.

Bury My Heart at Wounded Knee by Dee Brown. Four Winds Trading Company.

The Education of Little Tree by Forrest Carter. Four Winds Trading Company.

Julie of the Wolves by Jean Craighead George. Highsmith® Inc.

Kids Explore the Heritage of Western Native Americans. John Muir Publications.

The Nez Perce: A First Americans Book, Holiday House, Inc.

White Bead Ceremony by Sherrin Watkins. Council Oak Books.

Native Ways: California Indian Stories and Memories, Heyday Books.

Kids Explore the Heritage of Western Native Americans, John Muir Publications.

GENERAL MULTICULTURAL

Black, White, Just Right! by Irene

Trivas. Albert Whitman & Company.

Who Belongs Here? An American Story by Margy Burns Knights. Tilbury House, Publishers.

Talking Walls by Margy Burns Knight. Tilbury House, Publishers.

Respecting Our Differences by Lynn Duvall. Free Spirit Publishing, Inc.

A World of Children's Stories edited by Anne Pellowski. Friendship Press.

Celebrate! Holidays Around the World! Learning Works.

Less Than Half, More Than Whole by Kathleen and Michael Lacapa. Northland Publishing.

International Design Library. Stemmer House Publishers, Inc.

Thirty-Three Multicultural Tales to Tell, August House.

Ready-to-Tell Tales, August House.

- 6 -

Magazines & Newletters

Magazines and newsletters are great resources for a multicultural education, as well as sources for reviews of new products.

BLACK CULTURE, AFRICA & AFRICAN-AMERICANS

Just Us Books, 301 Main St, Orange NJ 07050. (201) 672-7701. FAX (201) 677-7570. This company specializes in books and learning materials for children which focus on the African-American experience.

There is a newsletter for young readers called *Harambee*, which is designed to help youngsters better understand African and African-American history and culture. Contemporary issues are covered and each issue focuses on a specific theme or aspect of the black experience. Published 6 times each school year, subscription $10. Single issue $2.

NATIVE AMERICAN

Cobblestone Publishing, 7 School Road, Peterborough NH 03458. (603) 924-7209. *Faces* magazine for children highlights people and cultures from over the world. The magazine is full of quality nonfiction articles, with each issue devoted to a special theme. Ages 9-15. Nine issues per year/ $21.95 subscription.

Heyday Books, PO Box 9145, Berkeley CA 94709. (510) 549-3564. FAX (510) 549-1889. *News from Native California: An Inside View of the California Indian World* is a quarterly newsletter with features, historical and current information articles, networking information, an events calendar, book reviews, and classifieds. Subscriptions are $17.50

for one years, 4 issues.

Native Experience, The, 7406 Waldron Ave., Temple Hills MD 20748. (319) 449-6730. Toll-free 1-800-652-6730. This group publishes *The Native American Experience Newsletter* which reviews and distributes books written by Native American authors or about Native American subjects. They have over 1,000 active titles and 10,000 backlist titles.

GENERAL MULTICULTURAL

Greenwood Publishing Group, Inc., 88 Post Road, W., PO Box 5007, Westport CT 06881-5007. This company publishes the *MultiCultural Review,* which is "Dedicated to a Better Understanding of Ethnic, Racial, and Religious Diversity." This magazine is a very useful tool for educators concerned about multicultural issues. It has special features, such as "Recommended and Not Recommended Books about Hispanics for Children and Adolescents," information about multicultural videos, and regular columns about the issues encountered in multicultural education. And, of course, many book reviews. Subscription: $59 per year.

Peoples Publishing Group, Inc, 230 West Passaic St., Maywood, NJ 07607. (201) 712-9185. FAX (201) 712-0045. Toll-free 1-800-822-1080. This company produces the *Multicultural Messenger,* the official newsletter of the International Multicultural Education Association. This publication was originally designed for K-12 educators, but is also informative for anyone, including parents and librarians, who are concerned about multicultural education. The newsletter contains important articles by national experts, case studies of school districts highlighting their needs and interests, and the inside story on sensitive issues. Subscription price, 9 monthly issues $175.

- 7 -

Teacher & Student Services

Special services for teachers and students, including teacher training ancial aid for students, are included in this chapter.

Amherst Educational Publishing, 30 Blue Hills Road, Amherst MA 01022-2220. (413) 253-7837. FAX (413)253-7024. Toll-free 1-800-865-5549. This company has a variety of publications for teaching in a diverse society. They have a brochure on this topic.

50 Activities for Managing Cultural Diversity by Teri Dickerson-Jones, includes reproducible activities, games, case studies, group discussion exercises, written exercises, and more, 300 pages in a three-ring binder, $139.95.

Mediation Across Cultures: A Handbook About Conflict and Culture by Selma Myers & Barbara Filner, helps people find effective solutions to conflicts generated by cultural misunderstandings and differences, $27.50.

Association for Childhood Education International, 11501 Georgia Ave, Suite 315, Wheaton MD 20902. (301) 942-2443. FAX (301) 942-3012. Toll-free 1-800-423-3563. This organization addresses race, ethnicity and culture in the classroom, and shows the need for educational policies, programs and practices that address the reality of diversity. The group has a checklist that helps to effectively identify and respond to diversity in the classroom. They also publish the book *Common Bonds: Anti-Bias Teaching in a Diverse Society* edited by Deborah Byrnes & Gary Kiger. This book examines the growing diversity in schools in a constructive, empowering manner. They identify various forms of cultural diversity and suggest ways that teachers can build inclusive classroom environments. 112 pages, $15.

Garrett Park Press, PO Box 190, Garrett Park MD 20896. (301) 946-2553. Their publication *Minority Organizations: A National Directory* (4th edition) is the most comprehensive guide to Black, Hispanic, Asian, and Native American organizations, $50. Another very useful resource is *Directory of Special Programs for Minority Group Members: Career Information Services, Employment Skills Banks, Financial Aid Sources* (5th edition) which is a comprehensive listing of over 1000 financial aid programs for minorities, and hundreds of special training programs, job placement, internship programs, etc, (especially for minorities and women), $30.

Minority Student Enrollments in Higher Education: A Guide to Institutions with Highest Percent of Asian, Black, Hispanic and Native American Students, lists 588 institutions where one minority accounts for at least 20 percent of the total enrollment. It also provides information on total enrollment in the school as well as the percent from each minority group, 93 pages, $15.

Intercultural Press, Inc., PO Box 700, Yarmouth ME 04096. They have the book *Education for the Intercultural Experience*, second edition, edited by R. Michael Page. It is based on two premises: (1) intercultural experiences are profoundly challenging and (2) education for such experiences require different strategies other than traditional practices. The book develops models for these new strategies.

Praxis Publications, Inc., PO Box 9869, Madison WI 53715. (608) 244-5633. This is a multicultural business enterprise that publishes educational and cultural literature. In addition, they provide training programs, consultation and technical assistance. Their publication, *How to Sponsor a Minority Cultural Retreat* by Charles A. Taylor, gives advice and resources for planning this type of retreat.

- 8 -

Cultural Events

Ethnic festivals and cultural activities are great resources for a multicultural education. I am including in this chapter the listings from the cities which responded to my inquiry. However, most cities have some sort of cultural events which would be wonderful learning activities for students. Check your local chamber of commerce or convention bureau for information in your area.

ASIAN CULTURE
ASIAN-AMERICANS

Los Angeles Convention & Visitors Bureau, 633 West Fifth St., Suite 6000, Los Angeles CA 90071. A variety of events are scheduled each year in January and February to celebrate Chinese New Year. Festivities include a reunion dinner on Chinese New Year's Eve, the Golden Dragon Parade, a community carnival, golf tournament, Chinese opera, and fireworks. Call (213) 617-0396 for schedule.

Thai New Year Celebrations are held at the Wat Thai Temple in North Hollywood, featuring traditional music, New Year songs, the Bathing of the Statue of Buddha, and the paying of respect to the elders and the monks. Call (818) 790-4200 for schedule.

Neisei Week Japanese Festival is a week-long festival in August with a parade, folk dancing, bands, exhibits, carnival and art exhibits. Call (213) 687-7193 for schedule and location.

Chinese Moon Festival and Street Fair celebrates the full moon of the eighth month of the Chinese lunar year with food and fun. Call (213) 617-0396 for schedule.

Korean Festival and Parade has drill marching teams, traditional dancers, Tae-Kwon-Do exhibitions and floats, carnival, chess tournament, and soccer games. Call (213) 730-1495.

San Francisco Visitors Bureau, 1900 Market St., San Francisco CA 94109. (415) 974-6900. San Francisco Chinese Chamber of Commerce, 730 San Francisco, San Francisco CA 94108. (415) 982-3000. Recorded message of events (415) 982-3071.

There is an annual celebration of Chinese New Years in San Francisco. There is a famous Dragon Parade, Carnival, Street Fair, Pageant, Fashion Show, special exhibits, music, and arts. Call or write the Chinese Chamber of Commerce for details.

Smithsonian Institution, Washington DC 20560. Each year the Smithsonian participates in the celebration of America's rich and diverse cultural heritage through observance of federally designated ethnic and women's heritage months. Heritage programs include special lectures, seminars, films, and related activities. May is designated Asian/Pacific Heritage month. For more information, write: Smithsonian Information, SI Bldg. Rm. 153, MRC 010, Smithsonian Institution, Washington DC 20560. (202) 357-2700.

BLACK CULTURE, AFRICAN-AMERICAN & AFRICA

Los Angeles Convention & Visitors Bureau, 633 West Fifth St., Suite 6000, Los Angeles CA 90071. Artists salute Black History Month (February). Call (213) 290-6636.

African Marketplace and Cultural Faire has over 350 arts and crafts merchants and live stages with 250 hours of continuous entertainment. This event has been held each August for the past 10 years, and continues through Labor Day. Call (213) 734-1164 for schedule and location.

New York Convention and Visitors Bureau, Two Columbus Circle, New York NY 10019-1890. French Caribbean Festival, FIAF celebrates Martinique, Dede Saint Prix, music and fun. Call (212) 355-6160.

Smithsonian Institution, Washington DC 20560. Each year the Smithsonian participates in the celebration of America's rich and diverse cultural heritage through observance of federally designated ethnic and women's heritage months. Heritage programs include special lectures, seminars, films, and related activities. February is Black History month. For more information, write to: Smithsonian Information, SI Bldg. Rm. 153, MRC 010, Smithsonian Institution, Washington DC 20560. (202) 357-2700.

EUROPEAN

Los Angeles Convention & Visitors Bureau, 633 West Fifth St., Suite 6000, Los Angeles CA 90071. Grand National Irish Fair and Music Festival at Santa Anita Racetrack features a horse show, bagpipe bands, dancing, Irish food and drink. Call (818) 985-2233 for schedule.

Annual Hungarian Festival at Alpine Village in Torrance features folk songs and dancing, gypsy orchestra and Hungarian goulash. Call (310) 327-4384.

HISPANIC

Los Angeles Convention & Visitors Bureau, 633 West Fifth St., Suite 6000, Los Angeles CA 90071. The traditional Mexican celebration, Dia de Los Muertos, Day of the Dead, features puppet shows, folklorico dancers, artisans and music. It is scheduled either in October or November every year. Call (213) 881-6444 for schedule.

Each year, historic Olvera Street celebrates Cinco de Mayo with shows, mariachi music and folklorico dancing. Call (213) 625-5045 for information.

In Watts, there's a joint celebration by Latino and African Americans for Cinco de Mayo, with a parade, booth, mariachi music, folklorico dancing, jazz, and rap music. Call (213) 564-9140 for a schedule.

Portland Cinco de Mayo, c/ Sharon McDonald, PO Box 1323, Portland OR 97207. (503) 222-9807. FAX (503) 292-9315. Portland's Cinco de Mayo festival is the largest bicultural festival held in the city. It's a festival of food, music and fun for the whole family held every year for several days surrounding May 5. It's held in the heart of Portland at Waterfront Park, along the Willamette River. The Ballet Folklorico, gem of Guadalajara, Mexico, perform their enchanting dances.

Smithsonian Institution, Washington DC 20560. Each year the Smithsonian participates in the celebration of America's rich and diverse cultural heritage through observance of federally designated ethnic and women's heritage months. Heritage programs include special lectures, seminars, films, and related activities. September 15-October 15 is Hispanic Heritage month. For more information, write to: Smithsonian Information, SI Bldg. Rm. 153, MRC 010, Smithsonian Institution, Washington DC 20560. (202) 357-2700.

NATIVE AMERICAN

Featherstone, PO Box 487, Brookings SD 57006. (605) 693-3193. FAX (605) 693-3189. Featherstone is a Native American owned company. The Bird family has many talents which are educational about Native Americans. Gordon Bird is a musician known far and wide for his traditional as well as rock 'n roll recordings. JoAnne Bird is a world reknown artist and sculptor. Jackie Bird is a world class champion hoop dancer. The family has performed internationally as a Native American dance team. For information about their shows and performances, please write or phone.

Gallup, New Mexico, Chamber of Commerce, PO Box 1395, Gallup NM 87301. (505) 722-2228. Each year since 1927, there's been an Inter-Tribal Indian Ceremonial in mid-August in and around Gallup, New Mexico. Thousands of Native Americans gather for four days of traditional dancing, chanting, parades, foods, games, arts and crafts. Over 20 Southwest tribes participate including Apache, Hopi, Navajo, and Zuni. This is the largest and most colorful Indian gathering open to the general public. What a great way to learn first hand traditional cultures and material art. For more information, call or write the Chamber of Commerce.

Los Angeles Convention & Visitors Bureau, 633 West Fifth St., Suite 6000, Los Angeles CA 90071. Native American Film Festival shows cinematic works by or about Native Americans which express their visions, diversity and ideas. Call (213) 221-2164 for a schedule.

The Natural History Museum has held an annual Native American Festival for the past 23 years in March. The festival features collector-quality artwork for sale, authentic cuisine, dance performances and entertainment. Call (213) 744-3488 for a schedule.

New York Convention and Visitors Bureau, Two Columbus Circle, New York NY 10019-1890. Thunderbird American Indian Mid-Simmer Pow-

Wow, in July, at the Queens County Farm Museum. Call (718) 347-3276.

Santa Fe, New Mexico, Visitors Bureau, PO Box 909, Santa Fe NM 87501. Toll-free 1-800-777-2489. Each year Santa Fe celebrates Indian Market during the middle of August. This market consists of numerous events, including the famous market on the Plaza downtown, where native craftspeople sell their wares in an open air atmosphere on the town square. Other events include auctions selling Indian arts, crafts and relics, as well as special exhibits at hotels across the city. There is no better way to see Indian art at its finest than to travel to Santa Fe for their annual Indian Market.

Smithsonian Institution, Washington DC 20560. Each year the Smithsonian participates in the celebration of America's rich and diverse cultural heritage through observance of federally designated ethnic and women's heritage months. Heritage programs include special lectures, seminars, films, and related activities. November is Native American Indian Heritage month. For more information, write to: Smithsonian Information, SI Bldg. Rm. 153, MRC 010, Smithsonian Institution, Washington DC 20560. (202) 357-2700.

GENERAL MULTICULTURAL

Milwaukee, Wisconsin, Visitors Bureau, 828 N. Broadway, Milwaukee WI 53202. (414) 273-3950. Or contact International Institute (414) 225-6220, sponsors of the Fair. Each November there's a Holiday Folk Fair to salute the many cultures of the world. Over 50 national groups present 3 days of continuous folk dancing, exhibits, singing, food, and folk arts. Some things that can be seen at this festival are: Swedish folk dancing, Japanese children's plays, Vietnamese food, Afro-American dance.

New York Convention and Visitors Bureau, Two Columbus Circle, New York NY 10019-1890. International Food Festival held annually. Call (212) 581-7029 for information.

- 9 -

Associations

This chapter lists ethnic and multi-ethnic organizations that offer resources that would be helpful to a multicultural education. Some of these organizations also offer seminars, training sessions, and conventions.

GENERAL MULTICULTURAL

Association for Childhood Education International, 11501 Georgia Ave, Suite 315, Wheaton MD 20902. (301) 942-2443. FAX (301) 942-3012. Toll-free 1-800-423-3563. This organization addresses race, ethnicity and culture in the classroom, and shows the need for educational policies, programs and practices that address the reality of diversity. The group has a checklist that helps to effectively identify and respond to diversity in the classroom. They publish the book *Common Bonds: Anti-Bias Teaching in a Diverse Society* edited by Deborah Byrnes & Gary Kiger. This book examines the growing diversity in schools in a constructive, empowering manner. They identify various forms of cultural diversity and suggest ways that teachers can build inclusive classroom environments. 112 pages, $15.

Ethnic Cultural Preservation Council, 6500 S. Pulaski Road, Chicago IL 60629. (312) 582-5143. FAX (312) 582-5133. This association helps ethnic group preserve art and educational centers in their communities. They aid in the exchange of information for the development of arts and humanities ethnic studies, provide grant information, and network on ethnic activities. They also sponsor seminars.

Ethnic Materials & Information

Exchange, Round Table, c/o American Library Association, Office for Library Outreach Services, 50 E. Huron, Chicago IL 60611. (312) 280-4295. FAX (312) 280-3256. Toll-free 1-800-545-2433. This association provides information on minority materials and educational programs. They maintain a library with directories, trade books, and filmstrips. They publish *The Directory of Minority/ Third World Publishers and Dealers* and *Multi-Ethnic Media: Selected Bibiographies*. They also hold an annual conference with the Midwinter ALA convention.

Garrett Park Press, PO Box 190, Garrett Park MD 20896. (301) 946-2553. Their publication *Minority Organizations: A National Directory* (4th edition) is the most comprehensive guide to Black, Hispanic, Asian, and Native American organizations, $50. Another very useful resource is *Directory of Special Programs for Minority Group Members: Career Information Services, Employment Skills Banks, Financial Aid Sources* (5th edition) which is a comprehensive listing of over 1000 financial aid programs for minorities. It also has hundreds of special training programs, job placement, internship programs, etc, (especially for minorities and women), $30.

International Society for Intercultural Education, Training, and Research, 808 17th St NW, Suite #200, Washington DC 20006. (202) 466-7883. FAX (202) 223-9569. This organization fosters intercultural education, training and research to foster communication, cooperation, and understanding between persons of differing cultural and racial backgrounds. They conduct a weeklong summer institute. Mailing lists are available. Their publications: *International Journal of Intercultural Relations,* which is quarterly; *International Society of Intercultural Education, Training & Research,* a bimonthly newsletter. They hold an annual congress with exhibits, an annual workshop, and an annual conference.

Multicultural Publishing and Education Council, 2280 Grass Valley Highway, #181, Auburn CA 95603. (916) 889-4438. FAX (916) 888-0690. This is a national networking and support organization for independent publishers of multicultural books and materials. This group attempts to provide an open forum for discussion of the issues of multiculturalism and to nurture multicultural publishing. MPWC promotes and encourages the publishing of books by and about people of color. The group holds an annual conference and regional workshops for its members. The conferences focus on topics such as marketing, publishing, distribution, educational networking, and emerging medias. Membership runs from $50 to $250 and all members receive the newsletter.

The *MPEC Newsletter* allows members to network with hundreds of publishers, writers, authors and editors of various races. There are reviews on books and videos, referral services, classified ads, and member news. Subscription alone is $48.

National Association for Ethnic Studies, Arizona State University, Department of English, PO Box 870302, Tempe AZ 85287-0302. (602) 965-2197. FAX (602) 965-3451. This group promotes research, study and curriculum design for ethnic studies. They present annual awards for ethnic studies. Their publications: *Ethnic Reporter,* semiannual newsletter; *Explorations in Ethnic Studies,* a semiannual journal; and *Explorations in Sights and Sounds,* which reviews books, nonprint media on ethnic studies. They hold an nnual convention.

National Council for Black Studies, Ohio State University, 208 Mount Hall, 1050 Carmack Road, Columbus OH 43210. (614) 292-1035. FAX (614) 292-7363. This association promotes and strengthens academic and community programs in black and/ or African-American studies. They sponsor essay contests and offer referral services. Their publications: *The Afrocentric Scholar: Journal of the National Council for Black Studies,* bimonthly; *Voices in Black Studies,* bimonthly newsletter. They hold an annual conference with exhibits.

National Council for Culture and Art, 1600 Broadway, Suite 611C, New York NY 10019. (212) 757-7733. This group's purpose is to provide exposure and employment opportunities for rural Americans, disabled Americans, and minorities. They sponsor art programs and concert series. Their publication: *Monarch Herald,* a quarterly newsletter. They hold an annual meeting.

Panamerican/ Panafrican Association, PO Box 143, Baldwinsville NY 13027. (315) 638-7379. FAX (315) 638-0778. This association promotes intercultural and interracial understanding. They hold seminars, educational encounters, art exhibits, and music recitals. They sponsor intercultural educational, cultural and economic exchange, such as the Royal Ethiopian Philharmonic Orchestra. They publish a periodic newsletter.

Society of Ethnic & Special Studies, Southern Illinois University at Edwardsville, Box 1652, Edwardsville IL 62026. (618) 692-2042. This association works to advance and preserve ethnic and special programs in secondary and post-secondary education. They sponsor workshops, seminars, publications, and projects. They publish a semiannual journal and hold an annual conference.

Society for the Study of Multi-Ethnic Literature of the U.S., University of North Carolina at Greensboro, Department of English, 132A McIver Bldg, Greensboro NC 27412. (919) 334-5484. This group wants to help educators enrich curricula with multicultural literature. They have a quarterly journal and an annual meeting.

- 10 -

Speakers, Seminars, Workshops, Conventions & Performers

There are many performers and speakers who are available for special events, or for an educational session. Seminars and workshops are also available, some through training manuals, and others through a training staff. This chapter also includes regularly scheduled conventions.

BLACK CULTURE AFRICAN-AMERICANS

African American Images, 1909 West 95th St, Chicago IL 60643. (312) 445-0322. Toll-free 1-800-552-1991. FAX (312) 445-9844. This company conducts workshop exploring topics relevant to black progress. For educators and parents, they have topics such as "Developing Positive Self-Images and Discipline in Children," "How to Improve Black Students' Academic Achievement," "SETCLAE (Self-Esteem Through Culture Leads to Academic Excellence)," "Motivating Black Youth for Success," "Lessons from History," and more. Call or write for details.

Lift Every Voice, Multicultural and Minority Source Materials Company, 16 Park Lane, Newton Centre MA 02159-1731. (617) 244-9808. FAX (617) 964-5432. This company has a *Children and Adult Multicultural Book Tape and Video Catalog*.

Speakers are available on Multicultural Education or Diversity.

HISPANIC CULTURE

California State University San Marcos, Center for the Study of Books in Spanish for Children and

Adolescents, San Marcos CA 92096-0001. (619) 752-4070. FAX (619) 752-4073. This organization holds an annual "Conference on Books in Spanish for Young Readers."

NATIVE AMERICANS

Featherstone, PO Box 487, Brookings SD 57006. (605) 693-3193. FAX (605) 693-3189. Featherstone is a wholly Native American owned company. The owners, Gordon and JoAnne Bird, are involved in many ways in the education of people about Native Americans.

The Bird family has many talents which are educational about Native Americans. Gordon Bird is a musician known far and wide for his traditional as well as rock 'n roll recordings. JoAnne Bird is a world reknown artist and sculptor. Jackie Bird is a world class champion hoop dancer. The family has performed internationally as a Native American dance team. For information about their shows and performances, please write or phone.

GENERAL MULTICULTURAL

Amherst Educational Publishing, 30 Blue Hills Road, Amherst MA 01022-2220. (413) 253-7837. FAX (413) 253-7024. Toll-free 1-800-865-5549. This company offers a wide range of products concerning multicultural diversity. This includes a series of workshops and training sessions.

The Human Diversity Workshop by George Banks, Ph.D., includes activities such as acknowledging points of view, learning about cultural groups and setting mutual goals. The workshop includes activities, facilitator notes, and written exercises. 300 page 2-volume set in 3-ring binders, $149.95.

Cultural Diversity: A Workshop for Trainers by Diane LaMountain and Bob Abramms, helps provide training on multicultural and diversity issues. It includes instructors guide, reference materials, lesson plans, and reproducible training aids. 398 pages in a 3-ring binder, $125.

University of Denver, Center for Teaching International Relations, Graduate School of International Studies, 2201 S. Gaylord St., Denver CO 80208. (303) 871-3106. FAX (303) 871-2456. The Center for Teaching International Relations offers courses and workshops that have teacher education concerning multicultural/diversity studies. There is an International Speakers Bureau with a wide range of speakers. Consulting services are also available.

- 11 -

Audio-Visual & Music Materials

Audio materials include recordings of ethnic music from various parts of the world, and some of which are for participation by children. Visual materials include videos of ethnics issues and visual presentation materials. Music materials include musical instruments for sale as well as music education.

ASIAN CULTURE & ASIAN-AMERICANS

Friendship Press, 475 Riverside Drive, Room 772, New York NY 10115. (212) 870-2588. This company has a complete catalog with books and other resources for global living, of which there are many for multicultural education.

In Their Own Words: Four Philippine Profiles is a 28 minute video that looks at the Philippines through the eyes of young people from different backgrounds. It includes a Teachers Guide. $39.95.

Kimbo Educational, PO Box 477, 10 North 3rd Ave., Long Branch NJ 07740. (908) 229-4949. Toll-free 1-800-631-2187. FAX (908) 870-3340. This company produces fine recordings for children.

Their Asian recordings for children include: *Contemporary Tinikling Activities* and *Tinikling Dances* which are about a Philippine island folk dance. Each tape is $10.95; and includes teacher's suggestions and diagrams; for ages 9+.

Smithsonian/Folkways Recordings, Office of Folklife Programs, 955 l'Enfant Plaza, Suite 2600, Smithsonian Institution, Washington DC 20560. (202) 287-3262. FAX (202) 287-3699. Their catalog has over 2,100 historic Folkways recordings which are listed by performer, geographic area and subject matter. There is music from all over the world and from numerous ethnic groups. Single cassettes are $10.95; CDs range from $8.50 to $14.

Their Asian culture recording include music from Asia and Oceania. Examples: *Music of Afghanistan, Music from South Asia, Cambodian Traditional Music, Chinese Classic Instrumental Music, Chinese Opera, Folk Music of India, Folk Music of Japan, Music of a Sherpa Village, Nepal*, and much more.

Video Presentations, 2326 6th Ave, Suite 230, Seattle WA 98121. Toll-free 1-800-458-5335. *Four Asian Folktales* shown as puppet plays: *Aniraku,* an Asian version of Rumpeltstiltskin; *Kyogne Stories,* humorous plays; *Brocade Slipper,* a Cinderella-type story; and *Undle Toad and the Jade Emperor,* a Vietnamese folktale about a traveler who journeys during a drought to plead with the emperor. All of the above is for ages 5-8 and available on two cassettes, $39.95.

White Swan Music, Inc., 1705 14th St, Box 143, Boulder CO 80302. (303) 443-8656. This company is a music source for world music, Native American, and ethnic vocals. They have African, Hispanic, Caribbean, Latin, India, Middle Eastern, Celtic, Asian, and more.

Music from Asia includes: *The Child Within* by Aldoush & The Human Exchange has Iranian songs with the poetry of Persian lyrics, cassette $9.95, CD $15.95; *Dark Fire* by Light Rain has Arabian fantasies to ignite the dancer in your soul, cassette $10.95, CD $15.95; *Spirit of India* by is music by Ravi Shankar, a master of the Indian sitar. Cassette $9.95, CD $18.95.

BLACK CULTURE
AFRICAN-AMERICANS
CARIBBEAN

African American Images, 1909 West 95th St, Chicago IL 60643. (312) 445-0322. Toll-free 1-800-552-1991. FAX (312) 445-9844. Their video *Up Against the Wall* is an excellent curriculum enhancement for teachers. *NBC Nightly News* said that it "teaches youth to feel positive about themselves." The video is $24.95.

Other videos available include: *Lessons From History: A Celebration in Blackness* that shows rich Black culture that goes beyond the slave trade, 120 minutes, $39.95; *Developing Positive Self-Images and*

Discipline in Black Children that discusses in detail effective strategies for parents, educators, and community leaders, 60 minutes, $29.95.

Black music education is available in the book *Shake It to the One That You Love the Best.* This is a songbook and tape set that includes 26 traditional childhood songs from African, African-American, Creole and Caribbean cultures. 55 pages, $15.95.

Better Place Publishing, Inc., 611 West Johnson Ave, Cheshire CT 06410. FAX (203) 250-7478. Toll-free orders 1-800-362-5437. This company has a set called *The Rainy Day Blues*. It is a hardcover book and audiocassette featuring the famous blues artist B.B. King. It has the story of a rained out baseball game and a kid's adventure that follows. This set helps kids find the silver lining on a rainy day, and it is also great for introducing kids the blues musical style. The book is 32 pages, the cassette is 20 minutes per side, $9.95 per set.

Chelsea House Publishers, PO Box 914, 1974 Sproul Road, Suite 400, Broomall PA 19008-0914. (610) 353-5166. Toll-free orders 1-800-362-9786. FAX (610) 359-1439. Send for the catalog called *Chelsea House Presents the Best in Black Studies* which features Black American history, profiles of great Black Americans, Black music, video collection, and more.

They have a series of *Traditional Black Music* which includes 15 hardcover titles and 7 paperback titles: *African Roots; Blues; Children's Songs; Gospel Songs; West Indian and Calypso*; etc. Each book is 64 to 80 pages, ages 10+, hardcover $15.95, paper, $7.95.

Their *Black Americans Audiobook Collection* has ten titles which are unabridged and unedited readings of the original texts. Titles include: *Frederick Douglass; Barbara Jordan; Colin Powell; Jackie Robinson; Malcolm X; Martin Luther King, Jr*; etc. Each audiobook is $15.95 and is recorded on two cassettes.

They have a series of video tapes called *Black American Video Collection.* Each video presents rare archival footage, photos and period music. Informative interviews with leading authorities and historians provide insights into each subject. There are 24 titles, including: *Muhammed Ali; James Baldwin; Jesse Owens; A History of the Civil Rights Movement; A History of Slavery in America;* etc. Each video is approximately 30 minutes long, $39.95.

Children's Circle®, 389 Newtown Pike, Weston CT 06883-9989. (203) 222-0002. Toll-free 1-800-KIDS-VID/ 1-800-543-7843. FAX (203) 226-3818. This company produces home videos based on outstanding children's books. Their video *Stories from the Black Tradition* won a Platinum Award from *The Best Toys, Books & Videos for Kids, 1994*. The video features folk and fairy tales from Africa and one inner-city story. The video includes: "Mufaro's Beautiful Daughters," "Why Mosquitos Buzz in People's Ears," "A Story—A Story," "The Village of Round and Square Houses," and "Goggles!" Ages 5+, 52 minutes, $14.95. Another video *Ezra Jack Keats Library,* is a collection of stories about Peter and his friends from this award-winning author, 44 minutes, $14.95.

Earwig Music, 1818 W. Pratt Blvd., Chicago IL 60626. (312) 262-0278. FAX (312)262-0285. *Norfolk Tales: Stories of Adventure, Humor and Suspense,* a Parents' Choice Gold Award Winner, by Bobby Norfolk, are adaptations of African and African-American tales with a message—place your faith in those who love you. Ages 4-8+, $10. *Why Mosquitos Buzz in People's Ears,* another Parents' Choice Gold Award Winner, by Bobby Norfolk, telling some highly animated African folk tales and Southern black stories, ages 5+, $10.

Friendship Press, 475 Riverside Drive, Room 772, New York NY 10115. (212) 870-2588. This company has a complete catalog with books and other resources for global living, of which there are many for multicultural education.

African Tales, is a 23-minute video that includes three African fables. It also contains a look at everyday life in Zaire. Study guide included, $29.95. *Ethiopia: The Land Beyond the Rivers* shows the rich history and culture of the Ethiopian people. It reveals the country beyond the famine and strife which is so often seen. Includes study guide,30 minutes, $27.95.

Caribbean video: *The Many Faces of the Caribbean* shows an overview of this region and its relationship with its neighbors to the north. Study guide included, 58 minutes, $39.95.

Highsmith® Inc., W5527 Highway 106, PO Box 800, Fort Atkinson, WI 53538-0800. Toll-free orders 1-800-558-2110. Toll-free customer service 1-800-558-3899. Toll-free FAX 1-800-835-2329. Highsmith is a distributor of high quality books and materials. They have a catalog called *Highsmith® Multicultural Bookstore™: Authentic Multicultural Books and Media* which has a wide selection of books for adults and children on multicultural subjects. There are children's storybooks, folktales and legends, activity books, young adult fiction and biography, literary criticism, business and finance, self help, social and political sciences, poetry, literature, culture, and much more.

Items to teach Black cultural music are: *Shake It to the One That You Love the Best: Play Songs and Lullabies From Black Musical Traditions* by Cheryl Warren Mattox, an audio tape and book featuring 26 of the most loved children's songs from Black culture, $15.95; *Lift Every Voice and Sing* by James Weldon Johnson, the national African American national anthem, $14.95.

Educational audiovisual materials are: *In Black and White: Six Profiles of African American Writers*, video series, $34.95 each; *Black Americans of Achievement,* an audio series, $15.95 each; *Black Americans of Achievement, Video Collections I and II,* $34.95 each.

Identity Toys Inc., 2821 N. 4th St., Milwaukee WI 53212. (414) 562-7776. They have games, puzzles, dolls and more which were designed with the Black child in mind.

<u>An interesting product line now available are the identity posters.</u> These are a great visual aid. There's the *African-American Child Poster,* showing a beautiful preschool Black child along with an original poem. There's also the *Legacy Poster,* which shows excerpts from Black history. Each poster is $6.95.

Inland Book Company, PO Box 120261, East Haven Ct 06512. (203) 467-4257. FAX 1-800-334-3892. *From Swing to Soul: An Illustrated History of African American Popular Music from 1930 to 1960,* traces the sounds of African American influence and innovation in mid-20th century music. It has biographies and photos of major personalties. Hardcover, $32.50. *From Cakewalks to Concert Halls: An Illustrated History of African American Popular Music from 1895 to 1930*, is a prize-winning book that traces the growth of this form of music from blackface minstrelsy to the big band era. Hardcover, $32.50, paper $21.95.

Lift Every Voice, Multicultural and

Minority Source Materials Company, 16 Park Lane, Newton Centre MA 02159-1731. (617) 244-9808. FAX (617) 964-5432. This company has a *Children and Adult Multicultural Book Tape and Video Catalog*.

Kimbo Educational, PO Box 477, 10 North 3rd Ave., Long Branch NJ 07740. (908) 229-4949. Toll-free 1-800-631-2187. FAX (908) 870-3340. This company produces fine recordings for children.

Their recordings for Black culture are: *Ethnic Dances of Black People,* which has eight native dances with instruction. It includes the Calypso (Trinidad), Shango (Africa), Samba (Brazil), Ibo (Haiti), Concumba (Africa), Yon Va Lou (Africa), and Maracatu (Brazil). 2 LP's or cassette & manual, $18.95.

Minnesota Historical Society Press, 345 Kellogg Blvd. West, St. Paul MN 55102-1906. (612) 296-7539. Toll-free orders 1-800-647-7827. FAX (612) 297-1345. This press has multicultural studies about Native American tribes (Sioux, Ojibway, Chippewa, Hidatsa), African American, Scandinavian, and Hispanic.

There is an audio tape, read by the author, on the book *Days of Rondo* by Evelyn Fairbanks. This book and tape are a warm reminiscence of St. Paul's thriving Black community in the 30's and 40's. Audio tape, 2 1/2 hours, 2 cassettes, $16.95.

There's also a poster *Minnesotans of African Descent* for $3.50.

African-American Music in Minnesota: From Spirituals to Rap, is a recording with a 64-page book with a wide range of music from secular to spiritual performed in Minnesota by African Americans today and in the past. CD $17.95, cassette $12.95.

Music for Little People Distributing, 50 Main St., Montpelier VT 05602. FAX (802) 223-5303. Order toll-free 1-800-223-6357. This company has a large selection of books, audio tapes, and video tapes with music for kids. This is a selection of items that are appropriate for multicultural education.

Items of interest for African-American education are: *I'm Gonna Let It Shine: A Gathering of Voices for Freedom* by Bill Harley, is a collection of 19 songs of the African-American Freedom Movement including "We Shall Overcome," "Oh Freedom," and more. Poems dealing with everyday life from a black perspective are found on *An Anthology of African American Poetry for Young*

People read by Arna BontempseSel.

A set that won the ALA Notable Children's Award and the *Booklist* Editor's Choice Award is *Shake It to the One You Love the Best: Play Songs & Lullabies from Black Musical Traditions*. This is a collection of dancing and singing from African, African-American, Creole and Caribbean cultures in jazz, reggae, gospel, rhythm & blues and classical styles. Cassette, book/ tape.

Bob Marley's mom, Ma Booker, weaves a spicy tale with uplifting tunes and storytelling about her beloved Jamaica in *Smiling' Island of Song*.

In video there's *African Story Magic* by Rickey O'Shon Collins.

One musical instrument available is the Talking Drum, from West Africa. A Unity Drum from Zimbabwe is also available.

National Archives, Trust Fund Boards, Washington DC 20408. Toll-free 1-800-788-6282. FAX (301) 763-6025. The National Archives has several videos for African American Studies, including the following: *Fighter for Freedom: The Frederick Douglass Story,* a 19-minute color video with historic photos and docudrama segments, $5; *From Dreams to Reality: A Tribute to Minority Inventors*, a 28-minute color video about minority inventors that have contributed to American science, technology, and medicine, $45; *The Negro Soldier,* a 42-minute black and white video from 1944 that shows the enormous contributions and sacrifices made by Black Americans, $45; *Booker T. Washington: The Life and Legacy*, an award-winning 32-minute color video showing the turning points of Washington's educational and political career, $45.

Public Media, 5547 N. Ravenswood Ave., Chicago IL 60640. Toll-free 1-800-826-3456. *African Journey* is a video about Luke Novack, a young man from Canada, who travels to Africa to visit his father and meets a young man his own age. The video, filmed in Zimbabwe, has wonderful landscapes. This is a good portrayal of two cultures side by side. Ages 10+, 174 minutes, 2 cassettes, $79.95.

Smithsonian/Folkways Recordings, Office of Folklife Programs, 955 l'Enfant Plaza, Suite 2600, Smithsonian Institution, Washington DC 20560. (202) 287-3262. FAX (202) 287-3699. Their catalog has over 2,100 historic Folkways recordings which are listed by performer, geographic area and subject matter. There is music from all over the world and from numerous ethnic groups. Single cassettes are $10.95; CDs range from $8.50 to $14.

There is an extensive collection from the African-American tradition. Examples: *African-American Folk Rhythms* by Ella Jenkins is a good introduction to African-American spirituals, *Glory of Negro History, Negro Folk Music of Alabama, African Musical Instruments, Black American Religious Music from Southeast Georgia, Country Gospel Song, Roots of Black Music in America,* and much more.

University of Illinois Press, 1325 South Oak St., Champaign IL 61820. Toll-free 1-800-545-4703. Their extensive list of Black Studies includes various books about traditional African-American music, such as: *Going to Cincinnati: A History of the Blues in the Queen City,* hardcover, $29.95; *Downhome Blues Lyrics: An Anthology from the Post-World War II Era,* $34.95; *Sinful Tunes and Spirituals: Black Folk Music to the Civil War,* paper, $16.95; *Voices of the Jazz Age: Profiles of Eight Vintage Jazzmen,* paper, $14.95.

White Cliffs Media, Inc., PO Box 433, Tempe AZ 85280. (602) 921-8039. Orders 1-800-359-3210. Several books and recordings of African American music: *Drum Gahu: Good-time Dance Music from the Ewe People of Ghana and Togo,* with energetic African village drumming, paper $15.95, cassette $12.95; *The Drums of Vodou,* with vodou-jazz and rhythms of Haitian spirit possession, paper $19.95, cassette $12.95; *The Music of Santería: The Oru del Ogbodu,* is a series of drummed rhythmic invocations to the Afro-Latin deities worshipped by followers of Santería, paper $19.95, cassette, $12.95; *Xylophone Music from Ghana,* featuring performances by African musician Joseph Kobom, paper $12.95, cassette $12.95; *Mandiani Drum and Dance: Performances Recorded in Africa,* showing the Mandiani tradition of music and dance that originated in Guinea and Sénégal, paper $19.95, cassette $12,95.

White Swan Music, Inc., 1705 14th St, Box 143, Boulder CO 80302. (303) 443-8656. This company is a music source for world music, Native American, and ethnic vocals. They have African, Hispanic, Caribbean, Latin, India, Middle Eastern, Celtic, Asian, and more.

Examples of their African

music are: *Logozo* by Angelique Kidjo is African polyrhythms with Western influences such as Caribbean sounds, cassette $12.95 CD $19.95; *Deep Forest* by Deep Forest, voices of the native African pygmies, remixed with European dance beats, cassette $12.95, CD $19.95; *Spirit of the Forest* by Baka Beyond of the Baka pygmies in the forest near the Cameron/ Congo border, cassette $9.95; CD $15.95; *Spirit of Africa* by Terry Oldfield explores the many faces of Africa from primal times, cassette $6.57, CD $15.95; *In African Eyes* by saxophonist Rene McLean from traditions of West Africa, cassette $9.95; CD $15.95. An excellent overview of African music today is *Africa ... Never Stand Still* with various artists performing on this two-cassette (or CD) set with a 48-page book which pictures and discusses the traditions, the rhythms, the instruments and the people. Cassette set, $29.95, CD set, $44.95.

CAJUN

Music for Little People Distributing, 50 Main St., Montpelier VT 05602. FAX (802) 223-5303. Order toll-free 1-800-223-6357. This company has a large selection of books, audio tapes, and video tapes with music for kids. This is a selection of items that are appropriate for multicultural education.

Cajun selection: *Le Hoogie Boogie: Louisiana French Music for Children* with Michael "Beausoleil" Doucet and his family and friends.

Rounder Records, 1 Camp St., Cambridge MA 02144. Toll-free 1-800-443-4727. This company is a distributor for *Le Hoogie Boogie: Louisiana French Music for Children* with Michael "Beausoleil" Doucet and his family and friends. Cassette $9.50. CD $15.

Smithsonian/Folkways Recordings, Office of Folklife Programs, 955 l'Enfant Plaza, Suite 2600, Smithsonian Institution, Washington DC 20560. (202) 287-3262. FAX (202) 287-3699. Their catalog has over 2,100 historic Folkways recordings listed by performer, geographic area and subject matter. There is music from all over the world and from numerous ethnic groups. Single cassettes are $10.95; CDs range from $8.50 to $14.

They have an excellent collection of Cajun and Zydeco music. Examples: *Cajun Fiddle, Bayou Memories, Cajun Accordion, Louisiana Creole Music,* and much more.

EUROPEAN CULTURE

Minnesota Historical Society Press, 345 Kellogg Blvd. West, St. Paul MN 55102-1906. (612) 296-7539. Toll-free orders 1-800-647-7827. FAX (612) 297-1345. This press has multicultural studies about Native American tribes (Sioux, Ojibway, Chippewa, Hidatsa), African American, Scandinavian, and Hispanic.

Norwegian-American Music from Minnesota: Old Time and Traditional Favorites is a recording with a 16-page book. LP Record $9.95, cassette $9.95.

Penfield Press, 215 Brown St., Iowa City IA 52245. (319) 337-9998. Toll-free 1-800-728-9998. FAX (319) 351-6846. This company "publishes books of ethnic interest and distributes books of similar interest from other publishers." There's titles about Norway, Sweden, Denmark, Finland, Iceland, Austria, Poland, Holland, Germany, Ireland, and more.

An educational video is *The Best of Sweden,* a 60 minute video giving a comprehensive overview of the many facets of Sweden, $29.95.

Smithsonian/Folkways Recordings, Office of Folklife Programs, 955 l'Enfant Plaza, Suite 2600, Smithsonian Institution, Washington DC 20560. (202) 287-3262. FAX (202) 287-3699. Their catalog has over 2,100 historic Folkways recordings listed by performer, geographic area and subject matter. There is music from all over the world and from numerous ethnic groups. Single cassettes are $10.95; CDs range from $8.50 to $14.

Their European recordings focus on the British Isles and Ireland. Examples: *English Concertina, British Broadside Ballads in Popular Tradition, English Folk Songs, Irish Folk Songs and Ballads, Singing Streets: The Childhood Memories of Ireland and Scotland,* and much more.

HISPANIC CULTURE SOUTH AMERICAN

Arte Público Press, The Americas Review, University of Houston, Houston TX 77204-2090. (713) 743-2998. FAX (713) 743-2847. Toll-free 1-800-633-ARTE. This is the oldest and largest publisher of Hispanic literature in the United States. Their extensive catalog includes autobiographies, fiction, poetry, drama, children's and adult literature, and more.

Videos include: *La Pastorela* by Luis Valdez, which is a Christmas fantasy starring Linda Ronstadt, Paul Rodríguez, Cheech Marín and other Chicano stars. 87 minutes, $24.95. Also available is *Zoot Suit* by Luis Valdez, the famous landmark play that was the first play by a Mexican-American every produced on Broadway. 100 minutes, $24.95.

HarperCollins, 10 E. 53rd St., New York NY 10022. (212) 207-7000. Toll-free 1-800-331-3761.Original songs from Latin countries are sung by Michele Valeri on *Mi Casa Es Su Casa/My House is Your House.* The listeners can learn Spanish words and phrases by listening to these sometimes silly, witty tunes. Ages 3-8, $11.

Highsmith® Inc., W5527 Highway 106, PO Box 800, Fort Atkinson, WI 53538-0800. Toll-free orders 1-800-558-2110. Toll-free customer service 1-800-558-3899. Toll-free FAX - 1800-835-2329. Highsmith is a distributor of high quality books and materials. They have a catalog called *Highsmith® Multicultural Bookstore™: Authentic Multicultural Books and Media* which has a wide selection of books for adults and children on multicultural subjects. There are children's storybooks, folktales and legends, activity books, young adult fiction and biography, literary criticism, business and finance, self help, social and political sciences, poetry, literature, culture, and much more.

Musical items for Hispanic culture: *Arroz Con Leche: Popular Songs and Rhymes from Latin America,* for preschool children, book $13.95.

Music for Little People Distributing, 50 Main St., Montpelier VT 05602. FAX (802) 223-5303. Order toll-free 1-800-223-6357. This company has a large selection of books, audio tapes, and video tapes with music for kids. There is a selection of items that are appropriate for multicultural education.

Appropriate selections for Hispanic material are: *Canta Conmigo (Sing With Me)* by Sue Young, with 14 original and traditional children's songs to teach Spanish words for numbers 1-10, names of clothing, fruit, greetings, etc. They also have *Rock 'n Learn Spanish, Tell Me a Cuento* and etc.

From South America, there's Pan Pipes from the land of Macchu Picchu in Peru. These pan pipes are made from bamboo and come in sets of 8 single-reed pipes and play a full octave in the key of C. It includes simple instructions. Ages 6+.

From Chile there's a Desert Rainstick, which was used by the Diaguita Indians to call the spirits of rain during a drought. Ages 4+.

Public Media, 5547 N. Ravenswood Ave., Chicago IL 60640. Toll-free 1-800-826-3456. *Sweet 15* is the story of 14-year-old Marta Delacruz looking forward to the coming-of-age celebration Mexican girls generally have at age 15. But her parents say they cannot have the celebration, and she finds that it's because her father is an illegal alien and may be discovered. Ages 8-10, 110 minutes, $29.95.

Smithsonian/Folkways Recordings, Office of Folklife Programs, 955 l'Enfant Plaza, Suite 2600, Smithsonian Institution, Washington DC 20560. (202) 287-3262. FAX (202) 287-3699. Their catalog has over 2,100 historic Folkways recordings listed by performer, geographic area and subject matter. There is music from all over the world and from numerous ethnic groups. Single cassettes are $10.95; CDs range from $8.50 to $14.

Their Hispanic collection includes music from Mexico, Central America and South America. *Suni Paz/ Alerta Sings Children's Songs for the Playground* with 13 songs from Latin America, the Caribbean and the U.S. Unusual instruments are used, such as the 10-stringed Andean charango and the rhythmic afuche. Other examples include: *Folk Songs of Mexico, Indian Music of Mexico, Music of Guatemala, Songs and Dances of Honduras, Argentine Dances, Latin American Folk Songs Sung in Spanish by Chago Rodrigo,* and much more.

JEWISH CULTURE
ISRAEL

HarperCollins, 10 E. 53rd St., New York NY 10022. (212) 207-7000. Toll-free 1-800-331-3761. *Zlateh the Goat and Other Stories* is a collection of seven stories containing fantasy and humor from the Eastern European Jewish tradition. Ages 10+, $10.

Music for Little People Distributing, 50 Main St., Montpelier VT 05602. FAX (802) 223-5303. Order toll-free 1-800-223-6357. This company has a large selection of books, audio tapes, and video tapes with music for kids. There is a selection of items that are appropriate for multicultural education.

Jewish selections: *What It Means to Be Jewish* which won a

Naird Indie Award. *Jewish Lullabies* shares the heritage of timeless songs children love that speak of Jewish heritage. Sung in English interwoven with Yiddish or Hebrew. *Celebrate with Cindy* has 28 holiday favorites, with songs from Rosh Hashana, Yom Kippur, Simchat Torah and Chanukah.

In video, there's the series *Shalom Sesame* which is 11 cassettes from Sesame Street the introduce the entire family to the land, people and culture of Israel. Each is in English with an introduction to Hebrew songs, numbers and letters.

Rounder Records, 1 Camp St., Cambridge MA 02144. Toll-free 1-800-443-4727. *Oy Chanukah!* with selections of Jewish lore and music. A woman describes how Chanukah is celebrated and someone else tells the story of Hannah and her sons, who were put to death for not renouncing their religion. Ages 10+, cassette $9.50, CD $15.

Shalom Sesame, PO Box 2284, South Burlington VT 05407. 1-800-428-9920. This company has a series of videos that introduce the land, people and culture of Israel. *Shalom Sesame Chanukah* celebrates the Festival of Lights and includes the Count, counting of course, in Hebrew, Ages 3-8; *The Land of Israel; The People of Israel; Sing Around the Seasons; Passover; Kids Sing Israel.* Each video $22.95.

Smithsonian/Folkways Recordings, Office of Folklife Programs, 955 l'Enfant Plaza, Suite 2600, Smithsonian Institution, Washington DC 20560. (202) 287-3262. FAX (202) 287-3699. Their catalog has over 2,100 historic Folkways recordings listed by performer, geographic area and subject matter. There is music from all over the world and from numerous ethnic groups. Single cassettes are $10.95; CDs range from $8.50 to $14.

Their Jewish collection includes: *Hebrew Folk Songs, Jewish Folk Songs of Europe, Shepherd and Other Folk Songs of Israel, Israeli Children's Songs, Hassidic Tunes of Dancing and Rejoicing,* and much more.

NATIVE AMERICANS

Chelsea House Publishers, PO Box 914, 1974 Sproul Road, Suite 400, Broomall PA 19008-0914. (610) 353-5166. Toll-free orders 1-800-362-9786. FAX (610) 359-1439. This publishing company has a catalog called *Chelsea House Presents the Best in Indian Studies* which features *Indians of North America, the Junior Library of American Indians, North American Indians of Achievement*, a video collection, and more. *The Indians of North America Video Collection* features video programs based on their book series with interviews of leading Native American scholars. There are ten titles, including: *The Apache; The Aztecs; The Yankton Sioux; The Cherokee; The Cheyenne; The Comanche; The Navajo;* etc. Each video is 30 minutes, $39.95.

Featherstone, PO Box 487, Brookings SD 57006. (605) 693-3193. FAX (605) 693-3189. Featherstone is a wholly Native American owned company. The owners, Gordon and JoAnne Bird, are involved in many ways in the education of people about Native Americans. One of the ways that they educate is through their recordings. *Dakota Language* by Agnes Ross (Santee Sioux) is an instructional aid to learn the Dakota language. Simple language material is presented in English, then in Dakota. Cassette $10. *The White Buffalo Calf Woman* is the legend of White Buffalo Calf woman as told by Martin High Bear, spiritual leader from Eagle Butte, South Dakota. Cassette $10.

All Nation Singers is 12 traditional songs from various Indian nations performed by the students of Flandreau Indian School. Cassette $10. *Music of the Plains* is traditional songs of the Plains performed on the flute by Gordon Bird. It includes Honor Songs, Round Dance/49 songs in all. The sounds of nature are in the background. Cassette $10.

Gordon Bird Sings ... Traditional Indian Songs is 12 songs from the Mandan, Hidatsa and Arickara Nations of North Dakota. It features the vocals of the late Pansy Parshall (mother of Gordon Bird) as well as JoAnne and Jackie Bird. It includes Honor Songs, Flag Song, Vietnam Veterans Song, and Grass Dance Songs. Cassette $10.

For information about their shows and performances, please write or phone.

Four Winds Trading Company, 685 South Broadway, Suite A, Boulder CO 80303. (303) 499-4484. Toll-free 1-800-456-5444. FAX (303) 499-6640. This company specializes in Native American music, literature, and products.

Kevin Locke, a world famous Lakota flute player and hoop dancer, is represented here. His tapes from this catalog are *Dream Catcher, Flash of the Mirror, Keepers of the Dream, Lakota Love Songs*, all available on cassette for $10 each. On CD, all of them are available except *Lakota Love Songs* for $15 each.

Another world famous Native American flute player is Carlos Nakai. His music is available from White Swan. *Ancestral Voices, Canyon Trilogy, Cycles, Earth Spirit, Journeys*, and more. Each cassette $10, CD $15.

Other Native American artists are represented, such as the group Inkuyo (from the Peruvian Andes), Ute flutist William Guitierrez, flutist John Huling, Dakota Sioux singer Joanne Shenandoah, Assiniboine-Dakota singer Georgia Wettline-Larsen, Navajo singer P.M. Begay, and many more.

Pow wow music is also available: *Gathering of Nations Pow Wow 1991* features Black Lodge Singers, Whitefish Bay Singers, Northern Wind Drum, Cathedral Lake Singers, and Sioux-Assiniboine Singers, cassette $10.60, CD $17; *Honor the Earth Powwow: Songs of the Great Lakes Indians* is a state of the art documentation of a Native American powwow, cassette $11, CD $17.

A presentation with not only music, but explanations in English is *Medicine Songs of the Native American Peyote Lodge* by Bearheart, a Lakota medicine man. The songs are both culturally significant and spiritually uplifting and accurate in every detail. Cassette, $10, CD $16.

A great way to teach both children and adults about Native American culture is through the talking tapes and storytelling, such as Kevin Locke's *The Flood and Other Lakota Stories*. He tells stories that reflect the values, belief systems, and social structure of his ancient heritage. 60 minutes, cassette only $11. *The Boy Who Lives with the Bears and Other Iroquois Stories* as told by Joe Bruchac was awarded the prestigious Benjamin Franklin Award in 1991 for Best Audio. This tape focuses on traditional stories and is told by native storytellers. 63 minutes, cassette only, $11. *Keepers of the Animals: Native American Animal Stories,* demonstrates the power of animals in Native American traditions. Two cassettes, $16.95. *Echoes of the Nights: Native American Legends of the Night Sky* are told by Tsonakwa and Dean Evans. The tribal stories from Hopi, Ojibway and other tribes are told with muffled drumbeats and haunting notes from an Indian flute and sounds from nature. 49 minutes, cassette $10, CD $16.

The famous book *Black Elk Speaks* is available as an audio book. Two 90-minute cassettes, $15.95. Also available in this format is *Black Elk: The Sacred Pipe,* two 90-minute cassettes, $15.95. *Native American Wisdom* with selections from Black Elk, Chief Joseph, Sitting Bull, and Red Cloud as they offer insights on Native American ways of living, learning, and dying. Background music is from Carlos Nakai's *Canyon Trilogy.* 80 minutes, cassettes, $10.95.

Videos available: *Wiping the Tears of Seven Generations* by Gary Rhine and Fidel Moreno shows a traditional Lakota ceremony, Wiping the Tears, in order to help bring their people out of the mourning for the past that has haunted them. This video won numerous awards. 58 minutes, $29.95. *More Than Bows and Arrows* narrated by N. Scott Momaday is an award-winning video that documents the often overlooked contributions the American Indians have given to the world. 1 hour, $19.95.

There's a video on Native American beadwork: *A Primer: Sewn Beadwork and Blanket Border Stitch,* $19.95. This accompanies a similar book for $2.95.

Greenfield Review Press, PO Box 308, 2 Middle Grove Road, Greenfield Center NY 12833. (518) 583-1440. FAX (518) 583-9741. They have an entire catalog called *North American Native Authors Catalog.* This 50-page catalog contains titles on legends, history, biographies, Native women, sacred traditions, dance and ceremony, crafts and skills, education and resources, fiction, poetry, and music.

Music available includes: *The Spirit of Crazy Horse: Songs for Leonard Peltier* is a collection of traditional and contemporary songs, $10.

Legends on cassette include a tape by one of my personal favorite artists: *The Flood* by Kevin Locke. This contains Lakota stories that reflect the values, beliefs and social structure of his people, $9.95; *Abenaki Cultural Heritage Celebration* has traditional tales, contemporary songs and flute music, $10.

Highsmith® Inc., W5527 Highway 106, PO Box 800, Fort Atkinson, WI 53538-0800. Toll-free orders 1-800-558-2110. Toll-free customer service 1-800-558-3899. Toll-free FAX 1-800-835-2329. Highsmith is a distributor of high quality books and materials. They have a catalog called *Highsmith® Multicultural Bookstore™: Authentic Multicultural Books and Media* which has a wide selection of books for adults and children on multicultural subjects. There are children's storybooks, folktales and legends, activity books, young adult fiction and biography, literary criticism, business and finance, self help, social and political sciences, poetry, literature, culture, and much more.

Their educational audiovisual materials include: *Indians of North America, Video Collection*, series of 10 about North American tribes, grades 4-10, each 30 minutes, $39.95; *Native American Animal Stories: Collected from Navajo, Cheyenne, Hopi, Kwaiuitl, Tlingit, and Iroquois Sources* by Gerald Hausman, an audio rendition of the helping and healing roles played by animals, $10.95; *American Indian Myths and Legends Volumes I and II,* by Richard Erdoes, tells of tribal tales of creation, love, heroes, war, animals, and tricksters, each $10.95. More audio and video material is available on Native American subjects which is not listed here.

Kimbo Educational, PO Box 477, 10 North 3rd Ave., Long Branch NJ 07740. (908) 229-4949. Toll-free 1-800-631-2187. FAX (908) 870-3340. This company produces fine recordings for children.

Their recordings about Native Americans include: *Authentic Indian Dances* for grades 3-6 that has the Corn Dance, War Dance, Rain Dance, and Strawberry Dance. LP or Cassette & Manual, $10.95.

Minnesota Historical Society Press, 345 Kellogg Blvd. West, St. Paul MN 55102-1906. (612) 296-7539. Toll-free orders 1-800-647-7827. FAX (612) 297-1345. This press has multicultural studies about Native American tribes (Sioux, Ojibway, Chippewa, Hidatsa), African American, Scandinavian, and Hispanic.

Ojibway Music From Minnesota: A Century of Song for Voice and Drum is a recording with a 16-page book with a sample of music spanning almost a century performed in Minnesota by Ojibway people. LP Record $9.95, cassette $9.95.

Music for Little People Distributing, 50 Main St., Montpelier VT 05602. FAX (802) 223-5303. Order toll-free 1-800-223-6357. This company has a large selection of books, audio tapes, and video tapes with music for kids. This is a selection of items that are appropriate for multicultural education.

There are numerous selections of Native American music and audio books for children in this catalog, such as: *The First Dog & Other Chippewa-Cree Stories* by Ron Evans. He tells stories from this timeless tribal tradition. *Coyote* by Joe Hayes is told from the New Mexican tradition about the poor coyote, who is always scamming and hustling and never quite pulling it off. *How Rabbit Tricked Otter & Other Cherokee Animal Stories* by Gayle Ross is a collection of Cherokee folk tales from the time when animals and people spoke the same language. *Coyote and Rock & Other Lushootseed Stories* by Vi Hilbert is stories from the people who inhabit Puget Sound in the Northwest Coast. Also available is *American Indian Songs & Chants.*

Smithsonian/Folkways Recordings, Office of Folklife Programs, 955 l'Enfant Plaza, Suite 2600, Smithsonian Institution, Washington DC 20560. (202) 287-3262. FAX (202) 287-3699. Their catalog has over 2,100 historic Folkways recordings listed by performer, geographic area and subject matter. There is music from all over the world and from numerous ethnic groups. Single cassettes are $10.95; CDs range from $8.50 to $14.

Their Native American collection includes: *American Indian Dances, Healing Songs of the American Indians, Music of the Pawnee, Songs and Dances of the Flathead Indians, Songs of the Chippewa, Turtle Mountain Music (North Dakota),* and much more.

Southwest Indian Foundation, PO Box 86, Gallup NM 87302-0001. (505) 863-4037. This nonprofit organization benefits the Indian peoples of the American Southwest. They have a catalog of interesting products, and the profits go directly back to the Indians themselves.

They have an *Indian Legend Tape Set* on which Cherokee Indian Jackie Crow Hiendlmayr retells ancient legends from many tribes, including the Mohawk, Cherokee, Hopi, and Sioux, $19.

White Swan Music, Inc., 1705 14th St, Box 143, Boulder CO 80302. (303) 443-8656. This company is a music source for world music, Native American, and ethnic vocals. They have African, Hispanic, Caribbean, Latin, India, Middle Eastern, Celtic, Asian, and more.

Native American music is represented by Kevin Locke, who is aworld famous Lakota flute player and hoop dancer. His tapes from this catalog are *Dream Catcher, Flash of the Mirror, Keepers of the Dream,*

Lakota Love Songs. They are all available on cassette for $9.95 each. On CD, they are all available with the exception of *Lakota Love Songs* , for $15.95 each. Another world famous Native American flute player is Carlos Nakai. His music is also available from White Swan. *Ancestral Voices, Canyon Trilogy, Cycles, Earth Spirit, Journeys,* and more. Each cassette $9.95, CD $13.95.

GENERAL MULTICULTURAL

Educational Activities Inc., PO Box 392, Freeport NY 11520. (516) 223-4666. Toll-free 1-800-645-3739. *One Voice for Children* by Jack Hartmant is an audio tape with songs such as *One Voice for Children, Respect Yourself and Others Too!, Everyone's Different,* and more. LP, $10.79.

Friendship Press, 475 Riverside Drive, Room 772, New York NY 10115. (212) 870-2588. *A World of Children's Songs* edited by Mary Lu Walker, 192 pages, hardcover, $19.95. This book has over 100 songs from around the world organized by continent. The songs include background cultural information. Most songs include at least one stanza in the original language with an easy pronunciation guide and simple musical arrangements.

Highsmith® Inc., W5527 Highway 106, PO Box 800, Fort Atkinson, WI 53538-0800. Toll-free orders 1-800-558-2110. Toll-free customer service 1-800-558-3899. Toll-free FAX 1-800-835-2329. Highsmith is a distributor of high quality books and materials. They have a catalog called *Highsmith® Multicultural Bookstore™: Authentic Multicultural Books and Media* which has a wide selection of books for adults and children on multicultural subjects. There are children's storybooks, folktales and legends, activity books, young adult fiction and biography, literary criticism, business and finance, self help, social and political sciences, poetry, literature, culture, and much more.

Educational audiovisual materials include: *Multicultural Peoples of North America, Video Series,* a collection of 15 productions that trace cultural groups which have emigrated from their homelands to North America, grades 4-10, 30 minutes each, $39.95 each. It portrays subjects such as: The Amish, Arab Americans, Central Americans, German Americans, Irish Americans, Italian Americans, Jewish Americans, Korean Americans, Puerto Ricans, etc.

Jordan Music Productions, MPO Box 490, Niagara Falls NY 14302. (416) 760-7664. Station M, Box 160, Toronto, Ontario Canada M6S 4T3. This company has available: *Sara Jordan™ Presents Celebrate the Human Race: Multicultural Songs & Activities for Children form Argentina, Brazil, Egypt, Nepal, Grand Canyon, Yosemite Valley, etc*. It includes reproducible paper dolls and costumes from around the world. Package is $8.99 for cassette and book.

Kimbo Educational, PO Box 477, 10 North 3rd Ave., Long Branch NJ 07740. (908) 229-4949. Toll-free 1-800-631-2187. FAX (908) 870-3340. This company produces fine recordings for children.

Their multicultural recordings include the award-winning *Joining Hands With Other Lands* which helps children learn through songs, games, and fingerplays what children are like in other parts of the world. Pre-K to grade 3, $10.95. There is also the *Children of the World* which won an award for 100 Best Products Picks for 1992. This recording teaches simple dances from around the world, as well as songs and activities, such as Polka, Tarantella, Maypole, Pata Pata, Samba and more. Ages 4-9, LP or Cassette and Guide, $10.95.

Also available is *Simple Folk Dances* with dances from Denmark, Dunkirk, etc. It is simple enough for preschool use. LP or Cassette & Manual, $10.95. *Multicultural Rhythm Stick Fun* shows rhythm stick activities set to folk songs from Puerto Rico, Ireland, Israel, Germany, Spain, Australia, Vietnam, Russia, Italy, West Africa, and more. Ages 4-9. LP or Cassette & Guide, $10.95.

Music for Little People Distributing, 50 Main St., Montpelier VT 05602. FAX (802) 223-5303. Order toll-free 1-800-223-6357. This company has a large selection of books, audio tapes, and video tapes with music for kids. This is their selection of items that are appropriate for multicultural education.

Travellin' with Ella Jenkins—A Bilingual Journey by Ella Jenkins. She has been performing for children all over the world. Her use of music from diverse cultures has made her an important figure in multicultural education. This tape has songs from around the world, including Hawaii, Switzerland, Israel, Puerto Rico, and Cajun.

Smithsonian/Folkways Recordings, Office of Folklife Programs, 955 l'Enfant Plaza, Suite 2600, Smithsonian Institution, Washington DC 20560. (202) 287-3262. FAX (202) 287-3699. Their catalog has over 2,100 historic Folkways recordings listed by performer, geographic area and subject matter. There is music from all over the world and from numerous ethnic groups. Single cassettes are $10.95; CDs range from $8.50 to $14.

Their collection from around the world includes: *Anthems of All Nations, Dances of the World's Peoples, Exotic Dances, Music of the World's Peoples, Volumes 1 through 5,* and much more.

Tapes 'n Books for Gifted Education, 314-350 Weinacker Ave., PO Box 6448, Mobile AL 36660. Toll-free 1-800-814-1548. FAX (205) 478-4755. Formerly *The Gifted Child Today Catalog*. This company has a video called *Multicultural Dimensions of Curriculum Design* that outlines three models that should be used to develop appropriate curriculum. Video $59.97 includes printed material. Audio version $13.97; add $3 for printed material with audio.

University of Illinois Press, 1325 South Oak St., Champaign IL 61820. Toll-free 1-800-545-4703. This press has an extensive list on Ethnic Studies, which includes *Barrio Rhythm: Mexican American Music in Los Angeles,* hardcover, $42.50, paper, $16.96.

White Swan Music, Inc., 1705 14th St, Box 143, Boulder CO 80302. (303) 443-8656. This company is a music source for world music, Native American, and ethnic vocals. They have African, Hispanic, Caribbean, Latin, India, Middle Eastern, Celtic, Asian, and more.

An excellent sampler of music from around the world is *Voices of Forgotten Worlds* which is a beautifully boxed set on the indigenous peoples of the world, with a 98-page book and two cassettes or CDs. You hear and read about Tuvan throat singers, pygmies, aborigines, Tibetan music, Inuit drum songs, and more. Music from 28 cultures produced in affiliation with the UN Center for Human Rites. Cassette set. $29.95, CD set, $34.95.

- 12 -

Material Culture

Material culture is the art and artifacts which a group of people use in their daily lives. This includes clothing, cooking utensils, religious artifacts, arts and crafts, etc. This chapter lists companies where these items can be obtained.

ASIAN CULTURE
ASIAN AMERICANS

Highsmith® Inc., W5527 Highway 106, PO Box 800, Fort Atkinson, WI 53538-0800. Toll-free orders 1-800-558-2110. Toll-free customer service 1-800-558-3899. Toll-free FAX 1-800-835-2329. Highsmith is a distributor of high quality books and materials. They have a catalog called *Highsmith® Multicultural Bookstore™: Authentic Multicultural Books and Media* which has a wide selection of books for adults and children on multicultural subjects. There are children's storybooks, folktales and legends, activity books, young adult fiction and biography, literary criticism, business and finance, self help, social and political sciences, poetry, literature, culture, and much more.

This company has a *China Kit* for studying material culture. This kit contains dolls, flute, chopsticks, abacus, and more with a resource guide, $175.

Museum of New Mexico Press, PO Box 2087, Santa Fe NM 87504. (505) 827-6454. FAX (505) 827-7308. This press has a lot of books about the Southwest, its Indian population, and the Hispanic influence. There are books about Pueblo Indians, Navajos, and New Mexican art and culture.

A book on East Indian culture is: *Mud, Mirror, and Thread: Folk*

Traditions of Rural India, which shows items from a world-class collection of rural Indian textiles, pottery, ornamentation, and folk decorations, 256 pages, 175 color plates, clothbound $60, paperbound, $45.

They also have a set of cards printed on handmade paper by a manual screening process that show the colorful textile traditions of rural India; 10 cards with envelopes for $15.

BLACK CULTURE AFRICAN-AMERICAN

A & B Distributors, Inc., 11-25 Brandford Place, Store #25B, Newark NJ 07102. Tel/ FAX: (201) 824-2556. Other location: 149 Lawrence St., Brooklyn NY 11201. (718) 596-3389. FAX (718) 596-0968. This company has a *Kwanzaa Gold Kit®* that includes kanara, candles, mat, cup, Kwanzaa kids postcard and a poster, $44.95.

Highsmith® Inc., W5527 Highway 106, PO Box 800, Fort Atkinson, WI 53538-0800. Toll-free orders 1-800-558-2110. Toll-free customer service 1-800-558-3899. Toll-free FAX 1-800-835-2329. Highsmith is a distributor of high quality books and materials. They have a catalog called *Highsmith® Multicultural Bookstore™: Authentic Multicultural Books and Media* which has a wide selection of books for adults and children on multicultural subjects. There are children's storybooks, folktales and legends, activity books, young adult fiction and biography, literary criticism, business and finance, self help, social and political sciences, poetry, literature, culture,

This catalog has several Kwanzaa sets, ranging from $34.95 to $105 depending on the elaborateness of the materials in the kit. Each set also contains the book *Kwanzaa: Everything You Always Wanted to Know But Didn't Know Where to Ask.* There's also a series of posters called *The Seven Principles of Kwanzaa* which are $10 each.

Also available for studying African material culture: *African Kit A* (traditional drum, batik art, carved ebony comb, African hut replica, African mask, and resource packet) $110; *African Kit B* (traditional cloth with proverbs in Swahili, stool, thumb piano, ankle bells, mock elephant hair bracelet, resource packet) $110; *The African Combination Kit,* with a collection of items from African Kit A and B, $197.

McCall Pattern Company, 11 Penn

Plaza, New York NY 10001. This company has patterns for "Authentic African Fashions." These patterns are for traditionally shaped headwraps, shawls, caftans, tunics, and hats such as the Kufi. There are patterns for men's, women's and children's clothing. They also make patterns for Kenya™ doll and doll clothes.

Music for Little People Distributing, 50 Main St., Montpelier VT 05602. FAX (802) 223-5303. Order toll-free 1-800-223-6357. This company has a large selection of books, audio tapes, and video tapes with music for kids. There is a selection of material items that are appropriate for multicultural education.

Their musical instruments available are the Talking Drum, from West Africa and a Unity Drum from Zimbabwe.

EUROPEAN CULTURE

Penfield Press, 215 Brown St., Iowa City IA 52245. (319) 337-9998. Toll-free 1-800-728-9998. FAX (319) 351-6846. This company "publishes books of ethnic interest and distributes books of similar interest from other publishers." There are titles about Norway, Sweden, Denmark, Finland, Iceland, Austria, Poland, Holland, Germany, Ireland, and more.

Material culture can be learned through their books: *Icelandic Patterns in Needlepoint,* with large scale charts and easy-to-follow instructions on how to make samplers, borders, repeating patterns, traditional symbols and floral designs, $29.95; *Fine Irish Crochet Lace,* over 50 illustrations plus instructions for making this especially fine type of lace, $4.95; *Tatting Hearts,* instructions for making 12 beautiful tatted hearts, $4.95.

HISPANIC CULTURE SOUTH AMERICA

Highsmith® Inc., W5527 Highway 106, PO Box 800, Fort Atkinson, WI 53538-0800. Toll-free orders 1-800-558-2110. Toll-free customer service 1-800-558-3899. Toll-free FAX 1-800-835-2329. Highsmith is a distributor of high quality books and materials. They have a catalog called *Highsmith® Multicultural Bookstore™: Authentic Multicultural Books and Media* which has a wide selection of books for adults and children on multicultural subjects. There are children's storybooks, folktales and legends, activity books, young adult fiction and biography, literary criticism, business and finance, self help, social and political sciences, poetry, literature, culture, and much more.

Materials items for Hispanic cultures include: *Huichol Indians of Mexico Kit,* which includes a God's Eye, Shaman's feathered arrow, yarn painting, picture postcard, children's rattle, carrying bag, earrings, and resource packet, $85.

From Central and South America they have: *Guatemala Kit,* includes a family of dolls, a piece of traditional cloth, a basket, traditional Shaman's incense, and a traditional fan for tortilla fires, $99. *Peru Kit* contains arpillera cloth, a traditional family of dolls, an Andean wind instrument, and a source packet, $105.

Music for Little People Distributing, 50 Main St., Montpelier VT 05602. FAX (802) 223-5303. Order toll-free 1-800-223-6357. This company has a large selection of books, audio tapes, and video tapes with music for kids. There is a selection of material items that are appropriate for multicultural education.

From South America, there is Pan Pipes from the land of Macchu Picchu in Peru. These pan pipes are made from bamboo and come in sets of 8 single-reed pipes and play a full octave in the key of C. It includes simple instructions. Ages 6+.

From Chile there's a Desert Rainstick, which was used by the Diaguita Indians to call the spirits of rain during a drought. Ages 4+.

NATIVE AMERICAN

Four Winds Trading Company, 685 South Broadway, Suite A, Boulder CO 80303. (303) 499-4484. Toll-free 1-800-456-5444. FAX (303) 499-6640. This company specializes in Native American music, literature, and products.

They have Native American flutes. Bear Flutes are six hole flutes, made from red cedar, $112. Coyote Oldman Flutes are generally five hole flutes of red cedar, $195. Flutebag, a soft tanned buckskin bag to protect the flute, is $48.

Sweet grass, cedar and sage are sacred plants that have been burned for centuries in ceremonies of clearing and blessing. 7" sage and cedar smudge stick, $3. 9" sage and cedar smudge stick, $5. White sage wands, $5.30. Sweet grass, $4 to $4.50 depending on length.

Gallup, New Mexico, Chamber of Commerce, PO Box 1395, Gallup NM 87301. (505) 722-2228. Each year since 1927, there's been an Inter-Tribal Indian Ceremonial in mid-August in and around Gallup, New Mexico. Thousands of Native Americans gather for four days of traditional dancing, chanting, parades, foods, games, arts and crafts. Over 20 Southwest tribes participate including Apache, Hopi, Navajo, and Zuni. This is the largest and most colorful Indian gathering open to the general public. What a great way to learn first hand traditional culture and material art. For more information, call or write the Chamber of Commerce.

Highsmith® Inc., W5527 Highway 106, PO Box 800, Fort Atkinson, WI 53538-0800. Toll-free orders 1-800-558-2110. Toll-free customer service 1-800-558-3899. Toll-free FAX 1-800-835-2329. Highsmith is a distributor of high quality books and materials. They have a catalog called *Highsmith® Multicultural Bookstore™: Authentic Multicultural Books and Media* which has a wide selection of books for adults and children on multicultural subjects. There are children's storybooks, folktales and legends, activity books, young adult fiction and biography, literary criticism, business and finance, self help, social and political sciences, poetry, literature, culture, and much more.

A book that teaches about Native American designs is: *Indian Designs* by David and Jean Villasenor, with 48 popular Native American designed used in decoration, $7.95.

McCall Pattern Company, 11 Penn Plaza, New York NY 10001. This company has patterns for "Heritage Dolls," which include a Native American doll.

Museum of New Mexico Press, PO Box 2087, Santa Fe NM 87504. (505) 827-6454. FAX (505) 827-7308. This press has a lot of books about the Southwest, its Indian population, and the Hispanic influence. There are books about Pueblo Indians, Navajos, and New Mexican art and culture.

A Native American material culture book of special interest is: *I Am Here: Two Thousand Years of Southwest Indian Arts and Culture*, which shows material culture from some of the finest collections of Southwest Indian art and artifacts of the nation, 256 pages, 90 color plates, 150 black and white photos, paperbound $39.95.

Naturegraph Publishers, Inc., Box 1075, 3543 Indian Creek Road, Happy

Camp CA 96039. (916) 493-5353. Toll-free 1-800-390-5353. FAX (916) 493-5240. This publisher specializes in books about nature and Native Americans.

One of their titles has been popular for a long time: *Indian Designs* by David and Jean Villasenor. This book has 48 designs that can be used for quilting, needlepoint, applique, clothing, pottery, crafts projects, and much more. There is an Indian design for virtually anything you need. $7.95.

Their ther books on Native American material culture are: *Indian Craft* by Chief "Dode" McIntosh and Harvey Shell, which shows the art and beauty of Indian craft illustrated and clearly written, $8.95; *Pomo Basketmaking: A Supreme Art for the Weaver* by Elsie Allen shows step-by-step directions for recreating beautiful and useful baskets, $6.95; *Making Native American Pottery* by Michael Simpson, shows how indigenous people gathered and processed clay, how to make designs and finishes, how to fire pottery without a kiln, and how to finish the pieces, $7.95.

Santa Fe, New Mexico, Visitors Bureau, PO Box 909, Santa Fe NM 87501. Toll-free 1-800-777-2489. Each year Santa Fe celebrates Indian Market during the middle of August. This market consists of numerous events, including the famous market on the Plaza downtown, where native craftspeople sell their wares in an open air atmosphere on the town square. Other events include auctions selling Indian arts, crafts and relics, as well as special exhibits at hotels across the city. There is no better way to see Indian art at its finest than to travel to Santa Fe for their annual Indian Market.

Southwest Indian Foundation, PO Box 86, Gallup NM 87302-0001. (505) 863-4037. This nonprofit organization benefits the Indian peoples of the American Southwest. They have a catalog of interesting products, and the profits go directly back to the Indians themselves.

Their catalog includes authentic handcrafted Indian items, such as Zuni bear fetish, beaded earrings, silver and turquoise jewelry, kachina dolls, and prints donated by R.C. Gorman as his gift to the Foundation.

GENERAL MULTICULTURAL

Hillcrest Press, Inc., 3412 W. MacArthur Blvd, Unit G, Santa Ana CA 92704. *Art as Technology: The*

Arts of Africa, Oceania, Native America & Southern California by Arnold Rubin and edited by Zena Pearlstone, is a scholarly and unusual study of the environmental, cultural, and utilitarian factors influencing the art of several cultures. These cultures include the Pueblo Indians, the Australian Aborigines, the Maya, the Maori, the Senufo, the Asante, the Plains Indians, and Southern California tribes.

Milwaukee, Wisconsin, Visitors Bureau, 828 N. Broadway, Milwaukee WI 53202. (414) 273-3950. Or contact International Institute (414) 225-6220, sponsors of the Fair. Each November there's a Holiday Folk Fair to salute the many cultures of the world. Over 50 national groups present 3 days of continuous folk dancing, exhibits, singing, food, and folk arts. Some things that can be seen at this festival are: Swedish folk dancing, Japanese children's plays, Vietnamese food, and Afro-American dance.

Stemmer House Publishers, Inc. 2627 Caves Road, Owings Mills MD 21117. (410) 363-3690. This company has a series called the International Design Library. These books are designs from various cultures, such as Nigerian, Aztec, Northwest Indian, Plains Indians, Peruvian textiles, Scandinavian, Chinese cut-outs, Egyptian, Japanese, etc. These books are essential to anyone studying the material culture of a particular group. There is a long list of these books, each $5.95.

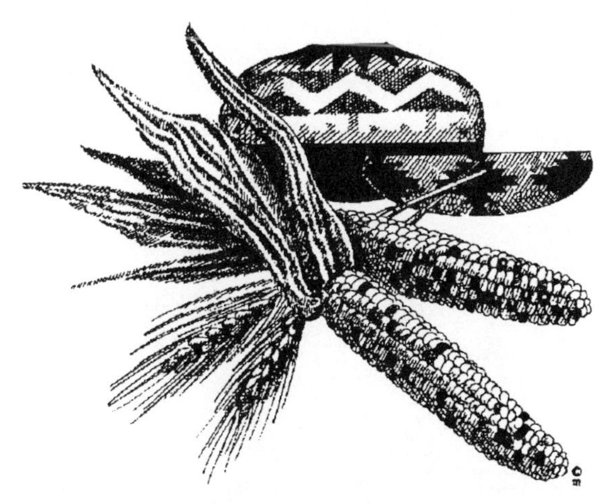

APPENDIX: Miscellaneous

BLACK CULTURE, AFRICAN-AMERICAN & AFRICA

Frank Schaeffer Publications, 23740 Hawthorne Blvd., Torrance CA 90505. (310) 378-1133. Bulletin Board Sets, each $6.95 per set: African-American Achievements, Famous Black Americans, African-American History, and Martin Luther King.

Friendship Press, 475 Riverside Drive, Room 772, New York NY 10115. (212) 870-2588. This company has a complete catalog with books and other resources for global living, of which there are many for multicultural education.

"African Art Cards" is a set of 16 cards, 4 each of 4 designs, with full-color postcards that are reproductions of original batiks from Uganda and a collage from West Africa, $4.95. *Those Remarkable Village People* with poems by Lucy Germany is a book of postcards depicting scenes of village life in the African nation of Malawi, $5.95.

Identity Toys Inc., 2821 N. 4th St., Milwaukee WI 53212. (414) 562-7776. They have games, puzzles, dolls and more which have been designed with the Black child in mind.

An interesting product line now available are the identity posters. There's the African-American Child Poster, showing a beautiful preschool Black child along with an original poem. There's also the Legacy Poster, that shows excerpts from Black history. Each poster $6.95.

There's also a coloring book and a calendar. *Color Me Proud®* coloring book has 50 pages to color plus 50 stickers. Ages 6+, $3. *Identity Kids® Calendar* is 12 months of African-American history, discovery, heroes, and things to do. Ages 7-12, $10.99.

McCall Pattern Company, 11 Penn

Plaza, New York NY 10001. This company has patterns for "Authentic African Fashions." These patterns are for traditionally shaped headwraps, shawls, caftans, tunics, and hats such as the Kufi. There are patterns for men's, women's and children's clothing. They also make patterns for Kenya™ doll and doll clothes.

NATIVE AMERICAN

Featherstone, PO Box 487, Brookings SD 57006. (605) 693-3193. FAX (605) 693-3189. Featherstone is a Native American owned company. The owners, Gordon and JoAnne Bird, are involved in many ways in the education of people about Native Americans. One of the ways that they educate is through their recordings. "Dakota Language" by Agnes Ross (Santee Sioux) is an instructional aid to to learn the Dakota language. Simple language material is presented in English, then in Dakota. Cassette $10.

The Bird family has many talents which are educational about Native Americans. Gordon Bird is a musician known far and wide for his traditional as well as rock 'n roll recordings. JoAnne Bird is a world reknown artist and sculptor. Jackie Bird is a world class champion hoop dancer. The family has performed internationally as a Native American dance team. For information about their shows and performances, please write or phone.

Four Winds Trading Company, 685 South Broadway, Suite A, Boulder CO 80303. (303) 499-4484. Toll-free 1-800-456-5444. FAX (303) 499-6640. This company specializes in Native American music and literature and products.

Council of the Rainmakers' Address Book features the art of David Dawangumptewa and Southwest Visions Address Book features the art of Helen Hardin. Each is about 8 x 9 with a color depiction of the artist's work on the front and inside there's a different color print for almost every letter of the alphabet. $12.95 each.

T-shirts, sweatshirts, and buttons are available with the Lakota phrase "Mitakyue Oyasin" which loosely means "We are all related." The phrase surrounds a NASA photo taken of the earth. Buttons, $2. T-shirts, $16. Sweatshirts, $27.

Frank Schaeffer Publications, 23740 Hawthorne Blvd., Torrance CA 90505. (310) 378-1133. This company has a Bulletin Board Sets about

Native Americans, $6.95.

McCall Pattern Company, 11 Penn Plaza, New York NY 10001. This company has patterns for "Heritage Dolls," which include a pattern for a Native American doll.

GENERAL MULTICULTURAL

Amherst Educational Publishing, 30 Blue Hills Road, Amherst MA 01022-2220. (413) 253-7837. FAX (413) 253-7024. Toll-free 1-800-865-5549. They have a *Multicultural Resource Calendar* for all grade levels. This is a comprehensive resource for information and instruction about important events for over 30 different cultures. Includes a resource guide, a black-line master calendar for each month, and a bibiography. $21.95.

EthnoGraphics, 417 Santa Barbara St., Suite B7, Santa Barbara CA 93101. (805) 899-8660. This company produces Multicultural Greeting Cards for Birthdays, Mother's Day, Father's Day, New Baby, Holidays (Kwanzaa, Chanukuh, Bar Mitzvah, Christmas) Graduation, and Friendship. They have a Hispanic collection, an African-American collection, a Native American collection, a Judaica collection, and an Asian collection.

Frank Schaeffer Publications, 23740 Hawthorne Blvd., Torrance CA 90505. (310) 378-1133. This company has a Bulletin Board Set about Children Around the World, $6.95.

Learning Works, PO Box 6187, Santa Barbara CA 93160. (805) 964-4220. Toll-free 1-800-235-5767. FAX (805) 964-1466. They offer multicultural rubber stamps for decorating name tags, invitations, announcements, art. Multicultural Girls or Multicultural Boys, $5.95 each.

Praxis Publications, Inc., PO Box 9869, Madison WI 53715. (608) 244-5633. This is a multicultural business enterprise that publishes educational and cultural literature and provides training programs, consultation and technical assistance. Their publication, *How to Sponsor a Minority Cultural Retreat* by Charles A. Taylor, gives advice and resources for planning this type of retreat.

Index

Bantam Books, 1540 Broadway, New York NY 10036. (212) 354-6500. Toll-free 1-800-223-6834.

Bess Press, PO Box 22388, Honolulu HI 96823. (808) 734-7159. FAX (808) 732-3627.

Better Place Publishing, Inc., 611 West Johnson Ave, Cheshire CT 06410. FAX (203) 250-7478. Toll-free orders 1-800-362-5437.

Black Classic Press, PO Box 13414, Baltimore MD 21203-3414. Orders toll-free 1-800-476-8870.

Booklines Hawaii, 94-527 Puahi St, Waipahu HI 96797. (808) 676-0116. FAX (808) 676-0634.

Books Nippan, 1123 Dominguez St, Suite K, Carson CA 90746. (310) 604-9701. FAX (310) 604-1134. Order toll-free 1-800-562-1410.

Boyds Mills Press, 815 Church St., Honesdale PA 18431. (717) 254-1164. FAX (717) 253-0179. Orders toll-free 1-800-949-7777.

Broderbund Software, PO Box 6125, Novato CA 94948-6125. Toll-free orders 1-800-521-6263.

California State University San Marcos, Center for the Study of Books in Spanish for Children and Adolescents, San Marcos CA 92096-0001. (619) 752-4070. FAX (619) 752-4073.

Calyx, PO Box B, Corvallis OR 97339. (503) 753-9384. FAX (503) 753-0515.

Carolrhoda, 241 1st Ave N., Minneapolis MN 55401. (612) 332-3344.

Center for Applied Research in Education, PO Box 430, West Nyack NY 10994. Division of Simon & Schuster. Order at: PO Box 11071, Des Moines IA 50336. Toll-free orders 1-800-947-7700.

Chelsea House Publishers, PO Box 914, 1974 Sproul Road, Suite 400, Broomall PA 19008-0914. (610) 353-5166. Toll-free orders 1-800-362-9786. FAX (610) 359-1439.

Childcraft Education Corporation, 20 Kilmer Road, Edison NJ 08818. (908) 572-6100.

Children's Book Press, 6400 Hollis St., Suite 4, Emeryville CA 94608. (510) 655-3395. FAX (510) 655-1978.

Children's Book Store Distribution, 67 Wall St., Suite 2411, New York NY 10005. Toll-free 1-800-668-0242.

Children's Circle®, 389 Newtown Pike, Weston CT 06883-9989. (203) 222-0002. Toll-free 1-800-KIDS-VID. Toll-free 1-800-543-7843. FAX (203) 226-3818.

Children's Press®, 5440 North Cumberland Ave., Chicago IL 60656-1494. Toll-free 1-800-621-1115. FAX 1-800-374-4329.

Clarion Books, 215 Park Ave South, New York NY 10009. (212) 420-5800.

Cobblestone Publishing, 7 School Road, Peterborough NH 03458. (603) 924-7209.

Consortium Book Sales and Distribution,

1045 Westgate Drive, St. Paul MN 55114-1065. Toll-free orders 1-800-283-3572. FAX (612) 221-0124.

Constructive Playthings, 1227 E. 119th St, Grandview MO 64030. Toll-free 1-800-832-0572.

Continental Press, 520 E. Bainbridge Street, Elizabethtown PA 17022. 1-800-233-0759.

Council Oak Books, 1350 East 15th St., Tulsa OK 74120. (918) 587-6454. FAX (918) 583-4995.

Crown Publishing Group, 201 E. 50th St., New York NY 10022. (212) 751-2600. Toll-free orders 1-800-726-0600.

DDL Books, Inc., 6521 NW 87th Avenue, Miami FL 33178. Toll-free orders 1-800-635-4276. FAX (305) 477-5632.

Dial, 375 Hudson St., New York NY 10014. (212) 366-2000.

Duke University Press, Box 90660, Durham NC 27708-0660. (919) 687-3600. Orders (919) 688-5134. FAX (919) 688-4574.

Dutton, 375 Hudson St., New York NY 10014. (212) 366-2000.

Earwig Music, 1818 W. Pratt Blvd., Chicago IL 60626. (312) 262-0278. FAX (312)262-0285.

Educational Activities Inc., PO Box 392, Freeport NY 11520. (516) 223-4666. Toll-free 1-800-645-3739.

Electronic Courseware Systems, Inc., 1210 Lancaster Drive, Champaign IL 61821. (217) 359-7099. FAX (217) 359-6578. Toll-free orders 1-800-832-4965.

Emory University, African Studies Association, Credit Union Building, Atlanta GA 30322. (404) 329-6410. FAX (404) 329-6433.

Eschar Publications, PO Box 1196, Waynesboro VA 22980.

Essential Learning Products, 2300 West Fifth Avenue, PO Box 2590, Columbus OH 43216-2590. (614) 486-0633. FAX (614) 487-2272.

Ethnic Cultural Preservation Council, 6500 S. Pulaski Road, Chicago IL 60629. (312) 582-5143. FAX (312) 582-5133.

Ethnic Materials & Information Exchange, Round Table, c/o American Library Association, Office for Library Outreach Services, 50 E. Huron, Chicago IL 60611. (312) 280-4295. FAX (312) 280-3256. Toll-free 1-800-545-2433.

EthnoGraphics, 417 Santa Barbara St., Suite B7, Santa Barbara CA 93101. (805) 899-8660.

Featherstone, PO Box 487, Brookings SD 57006. (605) 693-3193. FAX (605) 693-3189.

Feminist Press at the City University of New York, 311 East 94th St., New York NY 10128. (212) 360-5790. FAX (212) 348-1241.

Fisher Price, Inc., 636 Girar Ave., East

Aurora NY 14052. (716) 687-3395. FAX (716) 687-3238.

Franklin Watts, 95 Madison Ave., New York NY 10016. (212) 686-7070. Toll-free 1-800-621-1115. FAX 1-800-374-4329.

Free Spirit Publishing Inc., 400 First Avenue North, Suite 616, Minneapolis MN 55401-1730. (612) 338-2068. Orders toll-free 1-800-735-7323. FAX (612) 337-5050.

Four Winds Trading Company, 685 South Broadway, Suite A, Boulder CO 80303. (303) 499-4484. Toll-free 1-800-456-5444. FAX (303) 499-6640.

Frank Schaeffer Publications, 23740 Hawthorne Blvd., Torrance CA 90505. (310) 378-1133.

Friendship Press, 475 Riverside Drive, Room 772, New York NY 10115. (212) 870-2588.

Gallup, New Mexico, Chamber of Commerce, PO Box 1395, Gallup NM 87301. (505) 722-2228.

Garrett Park Press, PO Box 190, Garrett Park MD 20896. (301) 946-2553.

Golden Owl Publishing, PO Box 503, Amawalk NY 10501. (914) 962-6911. FAX (914) 962-0034. Toll-free 1-800-789-0022. Toll-free FAX 1-800-962-9101.

Golden Ribbon, PO Box 130222, Springfield Gardens NY 11413. Toll-free 1-800-722-8285.

Greenfield Review Press, PO Box 308, 2 Middle Grove Road, Greenfield Center NY 12833. (518) 583-1440. FAX (518) 583-9741.

Greenwood Publishing Group, Inc., 88 Post Road, W., PO Box 5007, Westport CT 06881-5007.

Gryphon House®, PO Box 275, Mt. Rainier MD 20712. Toll-free 1-800-638-0928. FAX (301) 779-6983.

HarperCollins, 10 E. 53rd St., New York NY 10022. (212) 207-7000. Toll-free 1-800-331-3761.

Harvard University Press, 79 Garden St, Cambridge MA 02138. Toll-free 1-800-448-2242. (617) 495-2480. FAX toll-free 1-800-962-4983.

Hasbro, 1027 Newport Ave., Pawtucket RI 02861. Toll-free 1-800-752-97555.

Heyday Books, PO Box 9145, Berkeley CA 94709. (510) 549-3564. FAX (510) 549-1889.

Highsmith® Inc., W5527 Highway 106, PO Box 800, Fort Atkinson, WI 53538-0800. Toll-free orders 1-800-558-2110. Toll-free customer service 1-800-558-3899. Toll-free FAX 1-800-835-2329.

Hillcrest Press, Inc., 3412 W. MacArthur Blvd, Unit G, Santa Ana CA 92704.

Holiday House, Inc., 425 Madison Ave., New York NY 10017.

Holloway House Publishing Co., 8060 Melrose Ave., Los Angeles CA 90046-

7082. (213) 653-8060. FAX (213) 655-9452.

Identity Toys Inc., 2821 N. 4th St., Milwaukee WI 53212. (414) 562-7776.

Inland Book Company, PO Box 120261, East Haven Ct 06512. (203) 467-4257. FAX 1-800-334-3892.

Intercultural Press, Inc., PO Box 700, Yarmouth ME 04096.

International Playthings, 120 Riverdale Road, Riverdale NJ 07457. (201) 831-1400.

International Society for Intercultural Education, Training, and Research, 808 17th St NW, Suite #200, Washington DC 20006. (202) 466-7883. FAX (202) 223-9569.

Jacaranda Designs, PO Box 7936, Boulder CO 80306. (303) 440-5235. FAX (303) 440-1361.

Jamestown Publishers, PO Box 9168, Providence RI 02940. (401) 351-1915. Toll-free 1-800-USA-READ. FAX (401) 331-7257.

Jewish Lights Publishing, Box 237, Sunset Farm Offices, Rt 4, Woodstock VT 05091. (802) 457-4000. FAX (802) 457-4004.

John Muir Publications, PO Box 613, Santa Fe NM 87504. (505) 982-4078. FAX (505)988-1680. Toll-free 1-800-285-4078.

Jordan Music Productions, MPO Box 490, Niagara Falls NY 14302. (416) 760-7664. Station M, Box 160, Toronto, Ontario Canada M6S 4T3.

Jossey-Bass Inc., Publishers, c/o Macmillan Publishing Group, 100 Front St, Box 500, Riverside NJ 08075-7500. Toll-free 1-800-257-5755. FAX toll-free 1-800-562-1272.

Just Us Books, 301 Main St, Orange NJ 07050. (201) 672-7701. FAX (201) 677-7570.

Kimbo Educational, PO Box 477, 10 North 3rd Ave., Long Branch NJ 07740. (908) 229-4949. Toll-free 1-800-631-2187. FAX (908) 870-3340.

KIT, Knowledge, Ideas & Trends, Inc., 1131-O Tolland Turnpike, Suite 153, Manchester CT 06040. (203) 646-0745. FAX (203) 646-3931.

Lathrop, Lee & Shephard Books, 1350 Avenue of the Americas, New York NY 10019. (212) 261-6500. Toll-free 1-800-843-9389.

Learning Company, 6493 Kaiser Drive, Fremont CA 94555. (510) 792-2101.

Learning Works, PO Box 6187, Santa Barbara CA 93160. (805) 964-4220. Toll-free 1-800-235-5767. FAX (805) 964-1466.

Lectorum Publications, Inc., 137 West 14th St, New York NY 10011. (212) 929-2833. FAX (212) 727-3035.

Lee & Low Books, 228 East 45th Street, New York NY 10017. (212) 867-6155. FAX (212) 338-9059.

Lift Every Voice, Multicultural and Minority Source Materials Company, 16 Park Lane, Newton Centre MA 02159-1731. (617) 244-

9808. FAX (617) 964-5432.

Little Brown & Company, Time Life Building, 1271 Avenue of the Americas, New York NY 10020. (212) 522-8700. Toll-free 1-800-343-9204.

Little Tikes, 2180 Barlow Road, Hudson OH 44236. Toll-free 1-800-321-0183.

Learning Resources, 675 Heathrow Drive, Lincolnshire IL 60069. Toll-free 1-800-222-3909.

Longstreet Press, 2140 Newmarket Parkway, Suite 118, Marietta GA 30067. (404) 980-1488. Toll-free 1-800-927-1488. FAX (404) 859-9894.

Los Angeles Convention & Visitors Bureau, 633 West Fifth St., Suite 6000, Los Angeles CA 90071.

Louisiana State University Press, PO Box 25053, Baton Rouge LA 70894-5053. (504) 388-8271. FAX (504) 388-6461.

Macmillan Publishing Company, Inc., 866 3rd Ave., 25th Floor, New York NY 10022. (212) 702-2000. Toll-free orders 1-800-257-5755.

Madame Alexandra, 615 West 131st St, New York NY 10027. (212) 283-5900.

Mattel, 333 Continental Blvd., El Segundo CA 90245. Toll-free 1-800-524-8697.

McCall Pattern Company, 11 Penn Plaza, New York NY 10001.

Middle Atlantic Press, Inc., 848 Church St., PO Box 1948, Wilmington DE 19899.

Milwaukee, Wisconsin, Visitors Bureau, 828 N. Broadway, Milwaukee WI 53202. (414) 273-3950. Or contact International Institute (414) 225-6220, sponsors of the Fair.

Mind*Play*, 160 West Ft. Lowell, Tucson AZ 85705. (520) 888-1800. FAX (520) 888-7904. Toll-free orders 1-800-221-7911.

Minnesota Historical Society Press, 345 Kellogg Blvd. West, St. Paul MN 55102-1906. (612) 296-7539. Toll-free orders 1-800-647-7827. FAX (612) 297-1345.

Morrow, 1350 Avenue of the Americas, New York NY 10019. (212) 261-6691.

Multicultural Publishing and Education Council, 2280 Grass Valley Highway, #181, Auburn CA 95603. (916) 889-4438. FAX (916) 888-0690.

Museum of New Mexico Press, PO Box 2087, Santa Fe NM 87504. (505) 827-6454. FAX (505) 827-7308.

Music for Little People Distributing, 50 Main St., Montpelier VT 05602. FAX (802) 223-5303. Order toll-free 1-800-223-6357.

National Archives, Trust Fund Boards, Washington DC 20408. Toll-free 1-800-788-6282. FAX (301) 763-6025.

National Association for Ethnic Studies, Arizona State University, Department of English, PO Box 870302, Tempe AZ 85287-0302. (602) 965-2197. FAX (602) 965-3451.

National Council for Black Studies, Ohio State University, 208 Mount Hall, 1050 Carmack Road, Columbus OH 43210. (614) 292-1035. FAX (614) 292-7363.

National Council for Culture and Art, 1600 Broadway, Suite 611C, New York NY 10019. (212) 757-7733.

National Council of Teachers of Mathematics, 1906 Association Drive, Reston VA 22091-1593. (703) 620-9840. FAX (703) 476-2970. Toll-free 1-800-235-7566.

Native Experience, The, 7406 Waldron Ave., Temple Hills MD 20748. (319) 449-6730. Toll-free 1-800-652-6730.

Naturegraph Publishers, Inc., Box 1075, 3543 Indian Creek Road, Happy Camp CA 96039. (916) 493-5353. Toll-free 1-800-390-5353. FAX (916) 493-5240.

New York Convention and Visitors Bureau, Two Columbus Circle, New York NY 10019-1890.

Northland Publishing, PO Box 1389, 2900 N. Fort Valley Road, Flagstaff, AZ 86001. (602) 774-5251. Toll-free 1-800-346-3257. FAX (602) 774-0592.

Open Hand Publishing, Inc., PO Box 22048, Seattle WA 98122-0048. (206) 323-2187. FAX (206) 323-2188.

Panamerican/Panafrican Association, PO Box 143, Baldwinsville NY 13027. (315) 638-7379. FAX (315) 638-0778.

Patail, 27324 Camino Capistrano #129, Laguna Niguel CA 92677. (714) 367-0530.

Pelican Publishing Company, PO Box 3110, Gretna, LA 70054. (504) 368-1175 customer service. FAX (504) 368-1195. Ordering toll-free 1-800-843-1724.

Penfield Press, 215 Brown St., Iowa City IA 52245. (319) 337-9998. Toll-free 1-800-728-9998. FAX (319) 351-6846.

Penguin USA, 375 Hudson St., New York NY 10014. (212) 366-2272.

Peter Bedrick Books, 2112 Broadway, Room 318, New York NY 10023. (212) 496-0751. Distributed by Publishers Group West, toll-free 1-800-788-3123.

Peoples Publishing Group, Inc, 230 West Passaic St., Maywood, NJ 07607. (201) 712-9185. FAX (201) 712-0045. Toll-free 1-800-822-1080.

Piñata Books, Arte Público, University of Houston, 4800 Calhoun, Houston TX 77204-2090. (713) 743-2841. FAX (713) 743-2847. Toll-free 1-800-633-ARTE.

Pleasant Company, 8400 Fairway Place, Middleton WI 53562. Toll-free 1-800-845-0005.

Portland Cinco de Mayo, c/ Sharon McDonald, PO Box 1323, Portland OR 97207. (503) 222-9807. FAX (503) 292-9315.

Praxis Publications, Inc., PO Box 9869, Madison WI 53715. (608) 244-5633.

Public Media, 5547 N. Ravenswood Ave.,

Chicago IL 60640. Toll-free 1-800-826-3456.

Rand McNally Maps, PO Box 7600, Chicago IL 60680. (709) 329-8100. Toll-free 1-800-333-0134. FAX (708) 673-5136.

Red Sea Press, Inc., 11-D Princess Road, Lawrenceville NJ 08648. (609) 844-9583. FAX (609) 844-0198.

Robert Rinehart Publishers, PO Box 666, Niwot CO 80544. Toll-free 1-800-352-1985.

Rounder Records, 1 Camp St., Cambridge MA 02144. Toll-free 1-800-443-4727.

San Francisco Visitors Bureau, 1900 Market St., San Francisco CA 94109. (415) 974-6900. San Francisco Chinese Chamber of Commerce, 730 San Francisco, San Francisco CA 94108. (415) 982-3000. Recorded message of events (415) 982-3071.

Santa Fe, New Mexico, Visitors Bureau, PO Box 909, Santa Fe NM 87501. Toll-free 1-800-777-2489.

Scholastic Inc., 555 Broadway, New York NY 10012. (212) 343-6100. Toll-free orders 1-800-325-6149.

Shalom Sesame, PO Box 2284, South Burlington VT 05407. Toll-free 1-800-428-9920.

Shambhala, c/o Random House, Inc., 400 Hahn Road, Westminister MD 21157. Toll-free 1-800-733-3000. In Hawaii, Alaska & Maryland, call toll-free 1-800-492-0782.

Smithsonian Folkways, 414 Hungerford Drive, Suite 444, Rockville MD 20850. (301) 443-2314.

Smithsonian/Folkways Recordings, Office of Folklife Programs, 955 l'Enfant Plaza, Suite 2600, Smithsonian Institution, Washington DC 20560. (202) 287-3262. FAX (202) 287-3699.

Smithsonian Institution, Washington DC 20560.

Society of Ethnic & Special Studies, Southern Illinois University at Edwardsville, Box 1652, Edwardsville IL 62026. (618) 692-2042.

Society for the Study of Multi-Ethnic Literature of the U.S., University of North Carolina at Greensboro, Department of English, 132A McIver Bldg, Greensboro NC 27412. (919) 334-5484.

Southwest Indian Foundation, PO Box 86, Gallup NM 87302-0001. (505) 863-4037.

Stemmer House Publishers, Inc. 2627 Caves Road, Owings Mills MD 21117. (410) 363-3690.

Tapes 'n Books for Gifted Education, 314-350 Weinacker Ave., PO Box 6448, Mobile AL 36660. Toll-free 1-800-814-1548. FAX (205) 478-4755.

Teacher Created Materials, Inc., 6421 Industry Way, Westminister CA 92683. (714) 891-7895. FAX (714) 892-0283. Toll-free 1-800-662-4321.

Temple University Press, Broad and Oxford Sts., Philadelphia PA 19122. (215) 204-

8787. Toll-free 1-800-447-1656. FAX (215) 204-4719.

Third World Press, PO Box 19730, Chicago IL 60619. (312) 651-0700. FAX (312) 651-7286.

Tilbury House, Publishers, The Boston Building, 132 Water St, Gardiner ME 04345. Trade accounts toll-free ordering 1-800-283-3572, Individual orders toll-free 1-800-582-1899. Distributed by: Consortium Book Sales and Distribution, listed in this book.

Tundra Books Inc., PO Box 1030, Plattsburgh NY 12901. (514) 932-5434. FAX (514) 484-2152. In U.S., orders should be sent to: University of Toronto Press, 340 Nagel Dr, Buffalo NY 14225. (716) 683-4547. FAX (416) 667-7832.

Tyco, 200 5th Ave, New York NY 10010. Toll-free 1-800-367-8926.

University of Denver, Center for Teaching International Relations, Graduate School of International Studies, 2201 S. Gaylord St., Denver CO 80208. (303) 871-3106. FAX (303) 871-2456.

University of Illinois Press, 1325 South Oak St., Champaign IL 61820. Toll-free 1-800-545-4703.

University of Oklahoma Press, 1005 Asp Avenue, PO Box 787, Norman OK 73070-0787. Toll-free 1-800-627-7377.

University Press of Mississippi, 3825 Ridgewood Road, Jackson MS 39211-6492. (601) 982-6272. Toll-free 1-800-737-7788. FAX (601) 982-6217.

University Press of New England, 23 South Main St, Hanover NJ 03755-2048. FAX (603) 643-1550. Order toll-free 1-800-421-1561.

U.S. Games, 179 Ludlow St., Stamford CT 06902-6912. (203) 353-8400. FAX (203) 353-8431. Toll-free orders 1-800-544-2637.

Ventura Educational Systems, Creative Teacher Division, 910 Ramona Avenue, Suite E, Grover Beach CA 93433-2154. Toll-free orders 1-800-336-1022.

Video Presentations, 2326 6th Ave, Suite 230, Seattle WA 98121. Toll-free 1-800-458-5335.

Viking Penguin, 375 Hudson St., New York NY 10014. (212) 366-2000. Toll-free 1-800-331-4624.

White Cliffs Media, Inc., PO Box 433, Tempe AZ 85280. (602) 921-8039. Orders 1-800-359-3210.

White Swan Music, Inc., 1705 14th St, Box 143, Boulder CO 80302. (303) 443-8656.

Winston-Derek Publishers Group Inc., PO Box 90883, Nashville TN 37209. Toll-free 1-800-826-1888 or 1-800-225-2256. FAX (615) 329-4824.

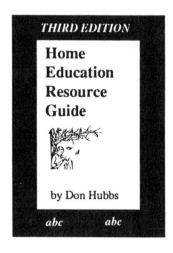

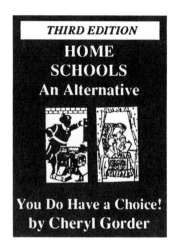

THE O.J. SYNDROME

CONFESSIONS OF AN ABUSER

by Rich Bean and Karen Crane

Every 12 seconds a woman is battered. 75% of women killed by the man they love are killed while trying to leave. It is estimated that as many as 4,000 women die each year at the hands of their domestic partners.

IT'S TIME TO DO SOMETHING ABOUT THE O.J. SYNDROME!

Rich Bean and his daughter, Karen Crane, have written a touching, yet true, story about Rich Bean's tragic years as an abuser and his recovery. It's a story that may spare someone from such horrors.

ISBN 0-933025-39-4 $11.95

Expanding Your Child's HORIZONS

A Whole Learning Activities Book for Parents & Teachers

by Dr. Art Attwell

Parents and teachers need to develop children who can become all they can be—children whose inquiring minds are appreciated and encouraged, whose creative ideas are not stifled. That's the purpose of whole learning.

This book contains over a hundred activities that can be easily used in the home or classroom with simple materials. The activities are designed to help children develop self-esteem, creativity, an inner focus, intuition, joy and pleasure in learning, and problem-solving skills.

ISBN 0-933025-28-9 $12.95

ORDER FORM